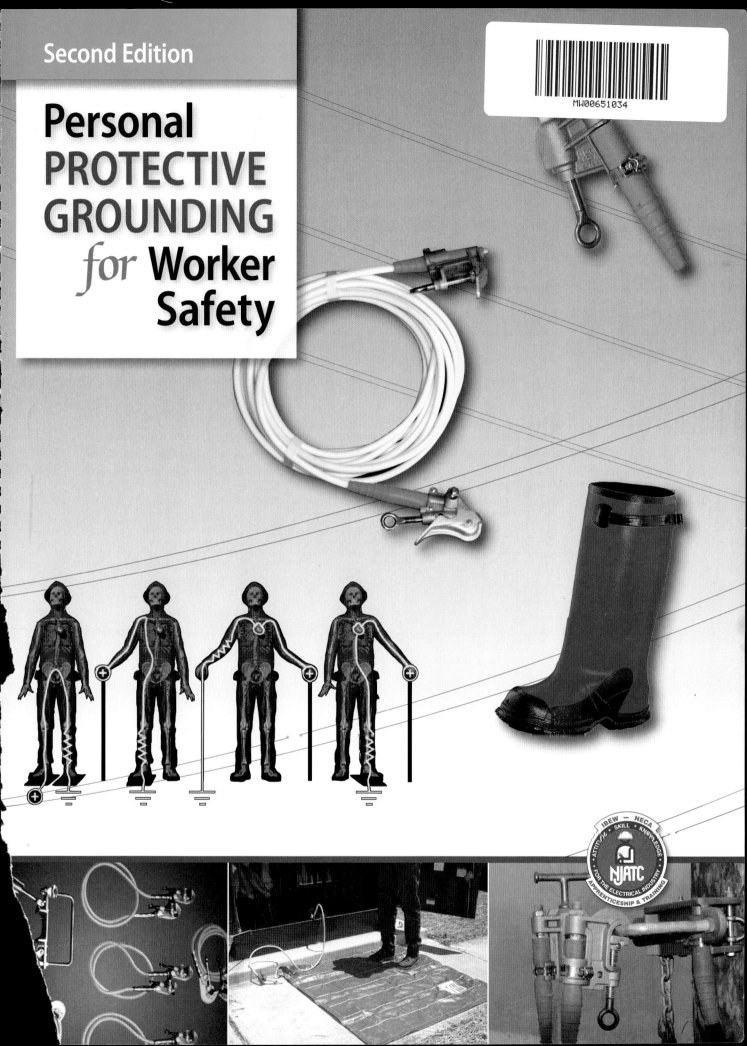

Second Edition

Personal
PROTECTIVE
GROUNDING
for Worker
Safety

MW00651034

IBEW — NECA
· ATTITUDE · SKILL · KNOWLEDGE ·
NJATC
· FOR THE ELECTRICAL INDUSTRY ·
APPRENTICESHIP & TRAINING

Printed in the United States of America

Contents

Contents

Acknowledgments

Principal Writer
    Clayton C. King, P. E.

Technical Writers
    Outside Education Committee Members
    George Gaudet, Mountain States Line Constructors
    Don Jamison, Missouri Valley Line Constructors Apprenticeship & Training
    Armando Mendez, California-Nevada Joint Apprenticeship Training
        Committee
    Howard Miller, American Line Builders JATC
    S.K. Pelch, Mountain States Line Constructors
    Bill Stone, Wilson Construction Co.
    Charles D. Young, Southwestern Line Constructors Area Joint
        Apprenticeship & Training Program
    Steve Uhl, Northeastern Joint Apprenticeship & Training Committee

Contributing Editors
    Steve Anderson, *electrical training ALLIANCE*
    Clark Blodgett, Southwest Line Constructors AJATC
    Michael I. Callanan, *electrical training ALLIANCE*
    Dr. Mary Capelli-Schellpfeffer, MD, MPA, CapSchell, Inc.
    Dan Dade, American Line Builders Apprenticeship Training Program
    Gary Fitzgerald, Southwestern Line Constructors Apprenticeship & Training
    Huel Gunter, Salisbury by Honeywell
    Harvey Haven, Northwest Line Construction Industry
    Jason Iannelli, *electrical training ALLIANCE*
    Everett Lewis, Northeastern Joint Apprenticeship & Training Committee
    Pete Lewis, Northeastern Joint Apprenticeship and Training
    James McGowan, Quanta Services, Inc.
    Virgil Melton, *electrical training ALLIANCE*
    Vladimir Ostrovsky, Salisbury by Honeywell
    Alex Trujillo, Southwestern Line Constructors AJATC

Features

Blue **Headers** and **Subheaders** organize information within the text.

Figures, including photographs and artwork, clearly illustrate concepts from the text.

INSTALLATION OF GROUNDS SEQUENCE

Before work begins on a line, circuit, or piece of equipment that is to be deenergized—or more specifically, electrically isolated and grounded—clearance must be obtained. Clearance is a documented statement from the operations supervisor to an authorized individual declaring that the line or equipment to be worked on has been disconnected from all power sources and deenergized. The circuit may be energized from static or induced sources and is not considered "dead" until it has been grounded. Circuits in close proximity to heavily energized circuits (usually 500 kilovolts) may cause the personal protective ground cable to draw an unacceptable arc during application.

There is a logical pattern to follow when installing personal protective grounds:
1. Test the voltage to verify that the system has been deenergized.
2. Locate and clean clamps for jumping, as well as connections.
3. Minimize the cable slack.
4. Fulfill the connection requirements.
5. Follow the assembly removal requirements.

Testing Voltage

The line, circuit, or piece of equipment must be tested for voltage before attempting installation. **See Figure 7-1.** Then by starting at the earth connection point, the voltage is maintained at 0 volts during the installation. It is at 0 volts because there is no current flow into the earth at this time, so no voltage is transferred to this connection point and the resistance of the earth does not come into the circuit.

The testing and order of installation and removal are specified by the U.S. Occupational Safety and Health Administration (OSHA). According to OSHA 29 CFR 1910, "Before any ground is installed, lines and equipment shall be tested and found absent of nominal voltage, unless a previously installed ground is present" (OSHA 29 CFR 1910.269(n)(5)) [8].

Voltage detection testing is the process of sensing voltage on a line—in other words, the process of determining whether line voltage is present. It is used to provide an indication of voltage levels and to ensure that the line has been deenergized or electrically isolated. Voltage detection should be used only as a secondary confirmation of electrical isolation and only after a clearance is in effect.

Several types of voltage detectors are commercially available. Three are in common use: the neon indicator, the hot-horn or noisy tester detector, and the multiple-range detector. Each voltage detector has its advantages and disadvantages. The worker should choose the detector most appropriate for the given circumstance.

The neon indicator is attached to the end of a live tool and positioned in the electrical field produced by the circuit. It produces a clear visual indication of an energized circuit. Neon indicators should be tested before and after each use. The neon voltage indicator provides a good visual indication; however, the detector is limited in application and may light up because of induced voltage from a nearby line.

The hot-horn or **noisy tester v   t detector** (NTVD), not to be co   d with the noisy tester buzzing   e, sounds an alarm to alert worke   at voltage is present. The NTVD   en used to check areas above o   ow ground and areas around sw   ear, substations, and overhead line   any NTVDs give a signal despite t   e of voltage on the circuit. Other   es of NTVDs are equipped with two   es to differentiate between circuit-a   ectro-magnetically induced voltages

This detector is battery ope   n, with 4.5 or 9 volts depending upon   voltage detector, and is attached to t   nd of a live-line tool. NTVD operat   may vary with the manufacturer; howev   ypically all that is involved is turning   e device and placing the detector in t   eld of the conductor. It is not necessa   o put the device in contact with the   uit and in some cases can be dangero   to do so— the NTVD should not t   ch circuits containing 33 kilovolts o   more. The manufacturer's specificatio   list the distances from the circuit th   ensure safe and accurate results. **See l   gure 7-2.**

Most NTVDs are supplie   with test and disconnect switches. T   instrument should be checked befor   and after each test to ensure proper and accurate usage.

There are several adv   ntages to using an NTVD. First, the worker can receive an approximation of the voltage without making contact with th   circuit. In addition, the NTVD is re   tively light and

Reminder
Always check local safety rules for PPE when using sticks.

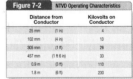

Figure 7-1   Testing the Line for Voltage

Figure 7-1. After isolation and before grounding jumpers are installed, OSHA law requires the line to be tested and found absent of nominal voltage.

Figure 7-2   NTVD Operating Characteristics

Distance from Conductor		Kilovolts on Conductor
25 mm	(1 in)	4
102 mm	(4 in)	13
305 mm	(1 ft)	26
457 mm	(1 ft 6 in)	33
0.9 m	(3 ft)	110
1.8 m	(6 ft)	230

Figure 7-2. Operating characteristics for the NTVD vary depending on the manufacturer but fall within a general range.

Reminder callouts emphasize safety and on-the-job tips.

Features

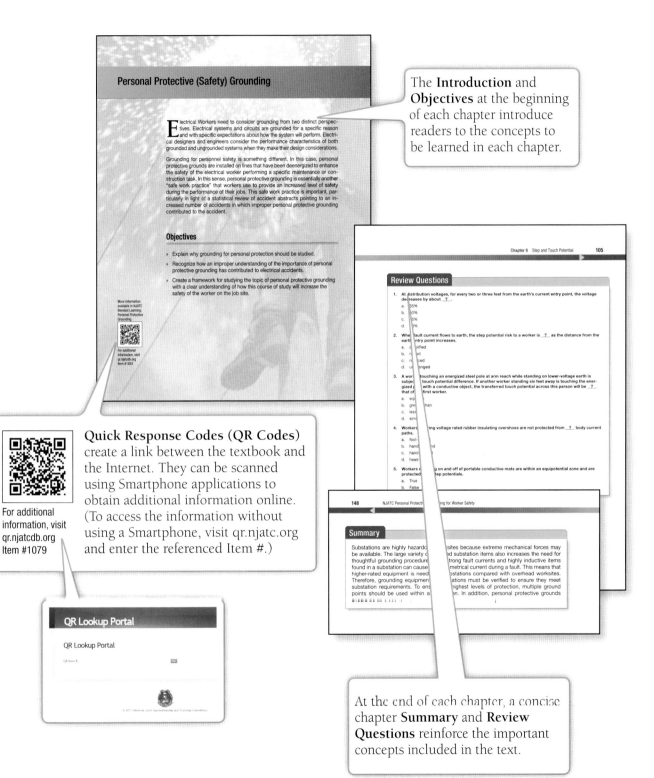

The **Introduction** and **Objectives** at the beginning of each chapter introduce readers to the concepts to be learned in each chapter.

Quick Response Codes (QR Codes) create a link between the textbook and the Internet. They can be scanned using Smartphone applications to obtain additional information online. (To access the information without using a Smartphone, visit qr.njatc.org and enter the referenced Item #.)

For additional information, visit qr.njatcdb.org Item #1079

At the end of each chapter, a concise chapter **Summary** and **Review Questions** reinforce the important concepts included in the text.

Introduction

Personal Protective Grounding for Worker Safety

Few other subjects provoke a stronger response from an experienced Electrical Worker than to inquire as to the preferred method of providing personal protective grounding. Grounding for safety is a key part of keeping a line worker safe during work on de-energized lines. It is becoming more difficult as the line voltage and currents increase, following the increase in customer demand. Much better protection is afforded to the worker when he/she is trained in safe grounding methods, as well as the work methods used to complete the assigned task.

Historically, there have been several attempts at establishing a "best-practice" for personal protective grounding. In the past, more workers were uninjured because of the extremely low probability that they were touching the line during the brief time it became re-energized during the work, rather than because of the protection scheme used. But low probability must not be relied upon. Clearly, there are several approaches that simply do not provide adequate levels of personal protection. Workers need to understand what the historical approaches have been and most importantly, why many of these approaches are often inadequate.

This course will provide the basics to maintain a worksite in as safe a manner as possible. However, it must be understood that situations may be encountered where complete safety cannot be 100% guaranteed. A worker knowledgeable in the basics will be able to assess such a situation and proceed in the safest manner available.

This class is offered as an introduction to new workers and as a refresher to experienced workers. Much has changed in recent years, personal protective grounding now has the weight of law following the OSHA regulation implementation. There can be penalties for the employees as well as the employer for violations. A worker will be able to understand grounding and be able to apply the principals after taking this course. The knowledge will help the understanding of grounding for safety, especially in those unusual situations where routine methods previously defined do not apply.

Introduction

Additional *electrical training ALLIANCE* Safety-Related Course Offerings and Training Materials

OSHA 500

This is the OSHA Trainer Course in Occupational Safety and Health Standards for the Construction Industry. It is designed to prepare instructors to teach the OSHA 10- and 30-hour Construction Industry Outreach Training Program. Diverse training methods are used and demonstrated including the *electrical training ALLIANCE* 10/30-hour course textbook, a video course related video package, as well as OSHA 10- and 30- hour PowerPoint presentations.

OSHA 502

This course is an option to retaking the OSHA 500. Successful completion of this course extends the instructor's authorization for an additional four years. Course focus is on the most recent updates to OSHA Construction Standards as well as the four leading hazards identified by OSHA. Participation in this class is limited to those who have previously successfully completed the OSHA 500 and hold authorization that has not expired.

Permit-Required Confined Space

This five-day class is a combination of OSHA's 3-day classroom-based course #226 and a two-day hands-on simulated entry training. Hands-on training includes air monitoring, ventilation, supplied-air respirators, self-contained breathing apparatus, retrieval, and other aspects of permit-required confined space entry.

Confined Space Entry (16 hours)

This course covers OSHA's 1910.146 Permit-Required Confined Spaces while highlighting 1926.21 Safety Training and Education, 1910.134 Respiratory Protection, and 1910.147 Control of Hazardous Energy (lockout/tagout). Students learn how to evaluate confined space hazards while practicing confined space entry using a tripod, winches, 2 D-ring full-body harnesses, supplied air, and other PPE. The course reviews the roles of the entrant, attendant, and entry supervisor.

OSHA 10- and 30-hour Course Training Materials
• NJATC 10- and 30-hour Instructors Guide and Student Workbook
• OSHA 29 CFR Part 1926 Construction Standard
• 10- and 30-hour Presentation CD

Scaffold Users and Erectors Training Materials
• Instructor Guide and Student Workbooks
• Videotape Package, DVD, PowerPoint CD
• Scaffold Users Manual

Consult the *electrical training ALLIANCE*'s website at www.electricaltrainingalliance.org or call 301.715.2300 for the latest course schedule.

Brief History of Grounding

No subject provokes such a strong response from an experienced Electrical Worker than the preferred method of providing personal protective grounding. Historically, there have been several attempts at establishing a "best practice" for personal protective grounding. Some approaches simply do not provide adequate levels of personal protection. Workers need to understand what these historical approaches have been and, most importantly, why they are inadequate.

Objectives

» Understand basic historical approaches to personal protective grounding.

» Describe the limitations of the "each-phase-to-separate-ground" method.

» Describe the limitations of the "each-phase-to-common-ground" method.

» Describe the limitations of the "phase-to-phase-to-ground" method.

» Describe the limitations of the "phase-to-phase-to-neutral" method.

Chapter 1

Table of Contents

HISTORICAL APPROACHES TO GROUNDING

Many methods used in the past to protect line workers were flawed, and accidents happened. More workers were probably protected by the low probability that a worker would contact the line at the precise instant during which the line was energized and before the line protection removed the voltage than were protected by their grounding techniques. Their grounds were applied without full appreciation of the current involved. It is only necessary to evaluate the worksite, not the entire circuit; however, full appreciation of the current and voltage potential of the circuit is crucial.

In the illustrations, the line worker presents a separate path for current flow through the worker. There is no low-resistance path in parallel with the worker. If a deenergized line accidentally becomes reenergized, the worker is in a separate path for current flow and may be injured or killed, depending upon the current. The pole-ground wire represents a completed path to earth through the worker. It could also represent the worker on a conductive steel structure.

In these procedures, it was believed that if the lines were connected to earth, the worker would be protected. But in each case, the worker's body presents a separate current return path through the earth, a potentially lethal condition.

Each Phase to Ground

When each phase is connected to a separate driven ground, several problems arise. First, resistance occurs between the grounds. Second, this method does not limit voltage drop across the worker. Third, long jumper, or lead, lengths appear. Finally, this method does not protect against step potential. **See Figure 1-1.**

Each Phase to Common Ground

When each phase is connected to a common ground, the result is a faster system reaction time than the previous method. There is also reduced resistance between phases compared with the prior method. However, connecting each phase to a common ground still presents problems. It does not reduce voltage drop across the worker and does not protect against step potential. **See Figure 1-2.**

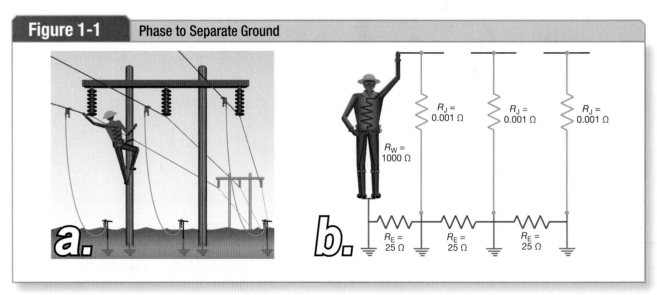

Figure 1-1   Phase to Separate Ground

Figure 1-1. (a) When each phase is connected to a separate ground, the worker completes a path to earth. (b) Separate driven ground rods allow resistance to occur between grounds. A worker's body presents a separate current return path through earth, creating a potentially lethal condition. R_J = jumper resistance, R_W = worker resistance, R_E = earth resistance.

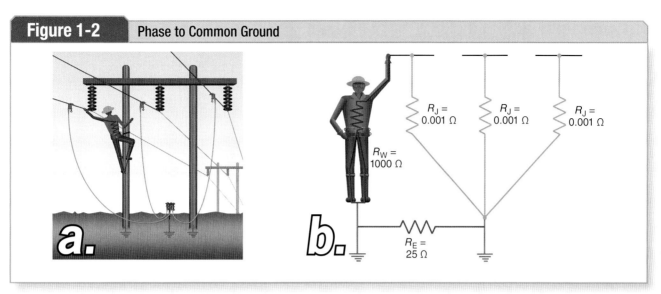

Figure 1-2. *(a) Connecting each phase to a common ground is an improvement to separate driven grounds, but problems remain. The pole ground presents voltage drop across the worker even if each phase is connected to a common ground. (b) A common ground for all phases allows high voltage to be transferred via the worker. R_J = jumper resistance, R_W = worker resistance, R_E = earth resistance.*

Phase to Phase to Ground

When jumpering from phase to phase, the number of jumpers, or leads, is reduced, as are multiple lead reactions. There is also minimum resistance between phases (rapid fault cleaning), making this method an improvement over those already discussed. Yet connecting from phase to phase to ground still does not reduce the voltage across the worker or protect against step potential. **See Figure 1-3.**

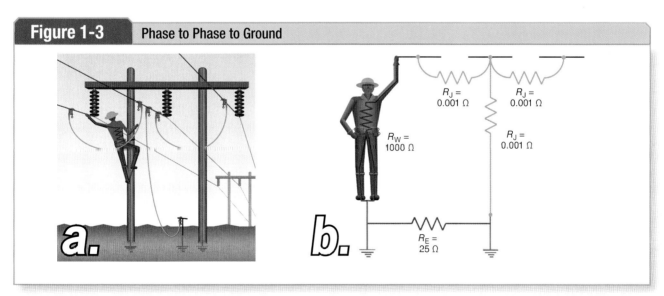

Figure 1-3. *(a) Jumpers placed from phase to phase to ground allow the pole ground to connect the worker to earth. (b) The phase-to-phase-to-ground method has the same problems that occur with phase-to-common-ground. This connection from phase to phase to ground does not protect workers. R_J = jumper resistance, R_W = worker resistance, R_E = earth resistance.*

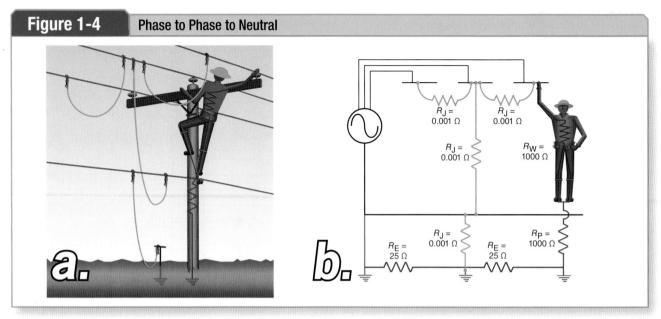

Figure 1-4. **(a)** *The grounding jumper connections from phase to phase and then to the grounded neutral offer low resistance paths, allowing maximum fault current flow back to the source. This ensures the fastest clearing time by the system's overcurrent protective equipment.* **(b)** *The worker, pole, and earth are resistors in series that provide a parallel fault current path to the source. With or without a pole ground wire, this technique does not provide adequate worker protection.* R_J = jumper resistance, R_W = worker resistance, R_E = earth resistance, R_P = pole resistance.

Phase to Phase to Neutral

Phase-to-phase-to-neutral is a traditionally-used variation of the phase-to-phase grounding technique. **See Figure 1-4.** The neutral is present on four wire types of distribution circuits and provides the best earth electrode and fault current return path. Because the neutral has multiple earth connections, ground fault relays in substations recognize faults of that type and operate quickly. Although the speed of the overcurrent protective devices is enhanced, the worker is at risk. During a fault event, the worker, pole, and earth form a parallel fault current path. This grounding method, although traditionally acceptable, does not provide adequate protection.

Bracket Grounding

Probably the most commonly-used yet incorrect protection scheme today is called bracket grounding, sometimes referred to as adjacent structure grounding. It places the protective grounds on either side of the worksite, at least one

structure away. The grounds are often placed several structures away, allowing the line worker to "work between grounds." This offers a sense of false security. **See Figure 1-5.** It protects the system but offers the worker little or no protection during line maintenance. This method has been around for a long time, and change from old ways is resisted. This makes bracket grounding the most dangerous grounding method still in use. **See Figure 1-6.**

Consider what happens if the de-energized line accidentally becomes reenergized and the worker is in contact with any possible voltage on the line. The fault current divides among all three paths, the two adjacent jumpers and the worker. The largest amounts flow through the lower resistance of the adjacent jumpers, but some pass through the path from worker to earth. The worker at 1,000 ohms is in series with the earth return path, assumed to be 25 ohms. With bracket grounding, the grounds on either side of the worker do not hold the line to 0 volts. As explained for series

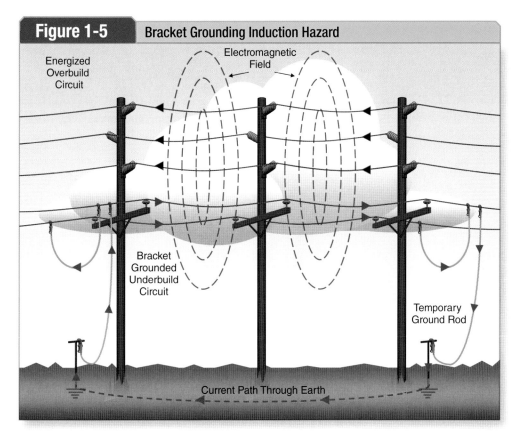

Figure 1-5   Bracket Grounding Induction Hazard

Figure 1-5. The current flow through the energized overbuild creates an electromagnetic field. The cutting action of this field induces a voltage in the isolated underbuild circuit. This is essentially an air-core transformer. When the second ground set is applied, a closed circuit is formed, resulting in a continuous circulating current.

circuits, a larger resistance develops a larger voltage drop. So a large percentage of the available voltage is across the worker.

Suppose that a system carries 7,200 volts. Under fault conditions, 80% of the system's 7,200 volts becomes the source voltage (E_{source} = 5,760 volts). Then assume the following:

$$R_E = 25 \ \Omega \text{ per path}$$
$$R_W = 1{,}000 \ \Omega$$
$$R_J = 0.001 \ \Omega \text{ per jumper}$$
$$I_F = 1{,}000 \text{ A}$$

where R_E is the earth resistance in ohms, R_W is the worker resistance in ohms, R_J is the jumper resistance in ohms, and I_F is the fault current in amperes. The adjacent jumper and interconnecting conductor resistances are low enough

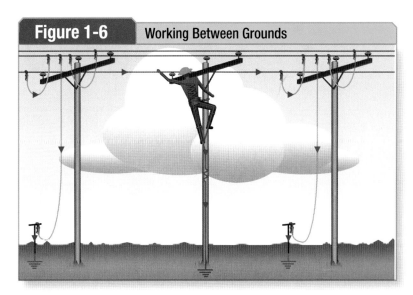

Figure 1-6   Working Between Grounds

Figure 1-6. In the past, it was mistakenly thought that by placing grounding sets at each side of the worksite, the worker would be protected if the current came from the left or the right. The reality is that some current will flow through every possible path.

that they can be ignored to better illustrate this circuit's lack of protection. **See Figure 1-7.**

These example resistances and currents can then be applied to an Ohm's Law calculation for bracket grounding. In this case, the current through each adjacent jumper to the worksite (per 1,000-amperes fault current available) is as follows:

$$I_J = \frac{E_{source}}{R} = \frac{5,760}{25} = 230 \text{ A}$$

The current through the worker is similarly calculated:

$$I_W = \frac{E_{source}}{(R_W + R_E)} = \frac{5,760}{(1,000 + 25)} = 5.6 \text{ A}$$

As expected, the major current flow was through the adjacent jumpers. However, a possibly lethal current flowed through the worker. Little or no protection was offered by this grounding scheme. The fault current was assumed to be only 1,000 amperes. Multiply the worker current by the number of kiloamperes available on an actual system, and

the danger becomes even more pronounced; for example, 10 kiloamperes, or 10,000 amperes, available gives a worker a current of 56 amperes.

Storm damage, line relocation or "shoo fly," and vandalism that make worksite grounding impractical remain the primary situations in which bracket grounding is still a viable option. In storm damage, place bracket grounding as near as practical to the worksite. The structures at the extremes of the repair section should have 3-phase grounding installed. Additional grounds should be used at the worksite when feasible.

Where a hazard exists or grounding at the first structure is not practical, grounds may be applied at the next adjacent structure. A transmission clipping crew has a minimum of two structures clipped between the crew and the conductor being sagged. When working on bare conductors, clipping crews work between grounds at all times. The grounds remain intact until the conductors are clipped in, except on deadend structures. Work on deadend structures requires grounding on all conductors.

Each conductor temporarily terminated at deadends or catch-off points is grounded

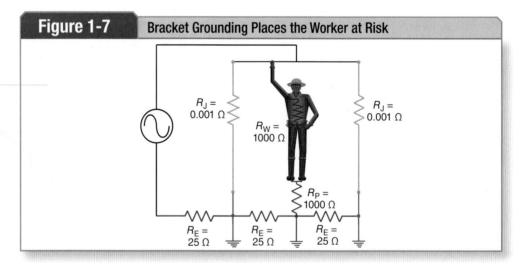

Figure 1-7   Bracket Grounding Places the Worker at Risk

Figure 1-7. Double-point or bracket grounding was a common practice placing grounding jumpers on both sides of the worksite. Historically, it was considered to be safe, although this method is now considered quite hazardous. The worker and pole are a parallel circuit branch and a fault current path. The grounding jumpers are also parallel branches. Parallel circuits have voltage drops across all branches. Branch currents divide in inverse proportion to the branch resistances. The body current through the worker can be lethal.

to the structure ground until the installation is completed. During clipping, the phase being clipped is grounded.

BEST-PRACTICE PROTECTION METHODS

The historically popular methods of grounding do not provide adequate personal protection. There are three methods of protection that keep a worker safe: isolation, insulation, and an equipotential zone.

Isolation

Physical isolation separates people from an area, typically using fences, barriers, or barricades to prohibit workers and the public from approaching grounded systems. A barrier can be any physical obstruction that is intended to prevent contact with energized lines or equipment or to prevent unauthorized access to a work area. **See Figure 1-8.**

However, this type of protection is not always feasible, depending on the physical constraints of the worksite or the type of work that needs to be completed.

Insulation

Insulation is designed to protect active contact workers against brush or incidental contact only. Examples of insulation are rubber and plastic materials, line hose, insulator covers, and pole covers. Personal insulation can be gloves, boots, and cover-ups. **See Figure 1-9.**

Insulation eliminates the current path through the worker. Unfortunately, like isolation, it is not always possible to use site-based insulation as protection. Still, workers should always be supplied with appropriate personal protective gear and should know how to put it on properly.

Equipotential Zone

An equipotential zone maintains voltage across the worker to an acceptably low level. It does this by placing the worker and a low-resistance shunt in parallel. This approach builds on the fundamentals of Ohm's Law.

Equipotential grounding is a basic grounding methodology like isolation and insulation, but of the three it is the one preferred for most work situations.

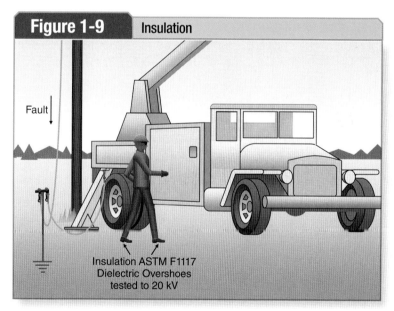

Figure 1-9 Insulation

Fault

Insulation ASTM F1117
Dielectric Overshoes
tested to 20 kV

Figure 1-9. Energization of the grounded overhead line will cause a voltage rise on the grounding equipment and the bonded truck. A voltage between this equipment and earth will be present. A worker wearing insulated overshoes has a barrier to current flow placed between his body and the earth. At most distribution voltages, overshoes of this type protect from hand to foot and from foot to foot potential differences. Insulation can also be provided by insulating mats or insulated platforms.

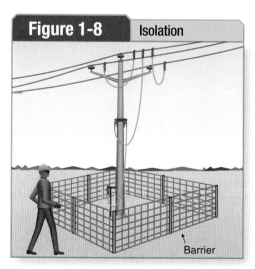

Figure 1-8 Isolation

Barrier

Figure 1-8. Isolation is created by a physical barrier that keeps people out of a work area.

Summary

Protection in the past was often the "luck of the draw." Because the methods used to protect line workers were flawed, accidents happened. Although many protection methods were used previously, none offered consistent, guaranteed protection. For example, low probability of contact at the time of reenergizing is not protection. Probably the incorrect protection scheme still in widest use today is called bracket grounding. A carryover from earlier times, bracket grounding, which places protective grounds on either side of the worksite, offers little or no protection and may be fatal. Three methods of protection keep a worker safe: isolation, insulation, and an equipotential zone.

Review Questions

1. Induction from a nearby energized circuit can cause circulating current to flow through the earth in closed circuit formed when the __?__ method of grounding is used.

    a. bracket

    b. phase-to-common-ground

    c. phase-to-phase-to-ground

    d. phase-to-separate-ground

2. Three grounding jumpers long enough to reach from the line conductors to the earth are required when the __?__ method is used.

    a. bracket

    b. phase-to-common-ground

    c. phase-to-phase-to-neutral

    d. working between grounds

3. Which of the following historical approaches to grounding provides the lowest cross-phase resistance and the most rapid fault clearing time?

    a. Each phase to neutral

    b. Phase to common ground

    c. Phase to phase to ground

    d. Phase to separate ground

4. Which one of the following is a commonly-used yet incorrect protection scheme that, because of worker resistance to change, is the most dangerous method still in use?

    a. Bracket grounding

    b. Cross phase grounding

    c. Each phase to common ground

    d. Single point grounding

5. By placing a low-resistance shunt in parallel with the worker, a(n) __?__ maintains voltage across the worker to an acceptably low level.

    a. adjacent structure grounding scheme

    b. equipotential zone

    c. isolation zone

    d. single point bonding method

Personal Protective (Safety) Grounding

Electrical Workers need to consider grounding from two distinct perspectives. Electrical systems and circuits are grounded for a specific reason and with specific expectations about how the system will perform. Electrical designers and engineers consider the performance characteristics of both grounded and ungrounded systems when they make their design considerations.

Grounding for personnel safety is something different. In this case, personal protective grounds are installed on lines that have been deenergized to enhance the safety of the electrical worker performing a specific maintenance or construction task. In this sense, personal protective grounding is essentially another "safe work practice" that workers use to provide an increased level of safety during the performance of their jobs. This safe work practice is important, particularly in light of a statistical review of accident abstracts pointing to an increased number of accidents in which improper personal protective grounding contributed to the accident.

Objectives

» Explain why grounding for personal protection should be studied.

» Recognize how an improper understanding of the importance of personal protective grounding has contributed to electrical accidents.

» Create a framework for studying the topic of personal protective grounding with a clear understanding of how this course of study will increase the safety of the worker on the job site.

More information available in NJATC Blended Learning: Personal Protective Grounding.

For additional information, visit qr.njatcdb.org Item #1823

Chapter 2

Table of Contents

IEEE 1048–2003

3.9 de-energized: Free from any electrical connection to a source of potential difference and from electric charge; not having a potential different from that of the earth.

TEMPORARY GROUNDING

Grounding for safety is a key part of keeping a line worker safe during work on deenergized lines. The term *deenergized* is defined by all national and international standards and the U.S. Occupational Safety and Health Administration (OSHA) as being "free from any electrical connection to a source of potential difference and from electric charge; not having a potential that is different from the potential of the earth." This is not the interpretation used by some maintenance craft and operations personnel, who may prefer the terms *electrically isolated* or *electrically isolated and grounded*. Deenergized lines are removed from their primary electrical source of energy by opening load current interrupting devices.

Temporary grounding is becoming more difficult as line voltage and currents increase, which is occurring because of an increase in customer demand. In the past, fewer workers were injured because of the extremely low probability that they would be touching the line during the brief time it became reenergized during the work, rather than because of the protection scheme used. But low probability must not be relied upon. Much better protection is afforded to the worker trained in safe grounding methods, as well as the work methods used to complete the assigned task. This training includes the basics of equipment selection and application, as well as an awareness of common accident causes and the knowledge of acceptable body current levels.

It must be understood that situations may be encountered in which safety cannot be guaranteed. A worker knowledgeable in the basics is able to assess such a situation and proceed in the safest manner available.

Much has changed in recent years; personal protective grounding has the weight of law following OSHA regulation implementation. There can be penalties for the employees, as well as the employer, for violations.

Grounding accidents have a variety of causes. The most common are human error, use of separate grounds, and induced voltages. Correction for human error is the duty of workers and the training they receive. The use of separate grounds and induced voltages is discussed in detail later.

Temporary Grounding Defined

A ground is a conducting connection, whether intentional or accidental, by which an electrical circuit or equipment is connected to earth or, in place of earth, to some other relatively large conductive body. When a temporary protective ground is used, a portable cable assembly carries current from a grounded piece of electrical equipment to earth. This assembly is sized to carry the maximum fault current and continuous current anticipated at the worksite. When a grounding system of personal protective and vehicle grounds is connected together at the worksite, this assembly is used to form an effective common ground.

Personal protective grounding is also applicable in distribution and transmission, in underground distribution substations, on trucks and digger derricks, and during line construction. Some of these applications are described later in the book.

Importance of Temporary Grounding

The primary use of protective grounds is to provide minimum risk for personnel while they are working on electrically isolated lines, buses, or equipment. **See Figure 2-1.** This is accomplished by reducing voltage differences at the worksite (voltage across the worker) to the lowest practical value in case the equipment or line being worked upon is accidentally energized. Another function of protective grounding is to protect against induced voltage from adjacent parallel energized lines or equipment.

COMMON CAUSES OF WORKER ACCIDENTS

There are several common causes of worker accidents:
- Human factors
- Use of separate grounds
- Contact with energized circuits
- Faults on adjacent circuits
- Lightning
- Equipment failure

Figure 2-1	Knowledge Can Save a Worker's Life

Figure 2-1. Why is it so important for a worker to understand temporary grounding? Because the knowledge can save that worker's life. More information available in NJATC Blended Learning: Personal Protective Grounding.

It is important for any Electrical Worker to understand these causes, as well as ways to avoid the potential accidents and injuries that may result.

Human Factors

Workers can play a role in causing incidents by doing one or more of the following:

- Ignoring induced currents or being unaware of induced voltage
- Accidentally reenergizing a line or piece of equipment
- Ignoring or overlooking lockout or tagout tags
- Inducing backfeed
- Incorrectly identifying a phase

Use of Separate Grounds

Historically, separate protective grounding connection points have been common. Connecting each phase to a separate driven ground creates problems related to resistance, voltage drop, and step potential, among others.

Contact with Energized Circuits

Contact with energized circuits typically occurs when the worker is unaware of circulating currents from adjacent energized lines. Energized lines are electrically connected to a source of potential difference or electrically charged so as to have a potential slightly different from that of earth in the vicinity.

Faults on Adjacent Circuits

A fault or fault current is a current that flows from one conductor to the ground or to another conductor because of an abnormal connection, including an arc, between the two conductors. At the worksite, voltage differences may appear because of induction from adjacent circuits.

Proper protective grounding results in a low-risk working environment. Low-resistance protective ground cables limit the voltage drop at the worksite to acceptable levels. Therefore, it is imperative that the protective ground cables be designed and assembled to handle the maximum acceptable levels of anticipated fault current.

Lightning

As with faults on adjacent circuits, voltage differences may appear at the worksite because of induction from lightning.

Equipment Failure

Equipment is designed not to fail, but when it does, failure can be caused by many things. Attention should be paid to checking equipment before and after use to mitigate problems.

RESULTS OF ACCIDENTS

Accidents on worksites can have varying results, from burns to heart fibrillation. Severe burns from high current passing through the body can occur both internally and externally. Heart fibrillation can result from low current passing through the chest area.

Flashover from an energized circuit, either to ground or to another phase, can cause flash burns. When a worker inserts his or her body or tools into the limited air space between a grounded and an energized line, it reduces the air insulation distance.

Danger exists if energized lines are near a work area. To protect against flash burns from high-voltage arcs, workers should wear arc-resistant clothing. They should also review the Institute of Electrical and Electronics Engineers (IEEE) guideline for minimum approach distances for energized lines and OSHA's Code of Federal Regulations (CFR).

Summary

When something is deenergized, it is free from any electrical connection to a source of potential difference and from electric charge. It does not have a potential different from that of the earth. Grounding for safety is a key part of keeping a line worker safe during work on deenergized lines. A ground is an intentional or accidental conducting connection by which an electrical circuit or equipment is connected to earth or another conductive body. Protective grounding prevents accidental death or injury from electrical shock. Grounding accidents are most commonly caused by human error, use of separate grounds, and induced voltages. More workers touching lines with higher voltage and currents is leading to more injuries than in the past.

Review Questions

1. OSHA defines the term __?__ as being, "free from an electrical connection to a source of potential difference and from electric charge; not having a potential that is different from the potential of the earth."

    a. cleared
    b. deenergized
    c. isolated
    d. locked-out

2. Proper temporary grounding will protect workers if lines are accidentally energized, but provides little or no protection against induced voltage from adjacent parallel lines.

    a. True
    b. False

3. When a grounding system of personal protective and vehicle grounds are connected together at the worksite, this assembly is used to form an effective __?__ ground.

    a. area
    b. common
    c. group
    d. sector

4. Ignoring induced currents or being unaware of induced voltages are considered to be types of human factor worker accidents.

    a. True
    b. False

5. Voltage drop at the worksite is limited to acceptable levels by __?__.

    a. low resistance protective ground cables
    b. proper lockout tagout procedures
    c. separate ground rods
    d. substation grounding switches

Body Currents

Early in their electrical careers, workers learn the hazards of working on or near electrical circuits and equipment. Today, the greatest electrical hazards they confront are the risks of electrical shock and arc flash and blasts. Only recently have Electrical Workers begun to understand what occurs during an electrical arc blast or flash, and this knowledge is affecting the way people work on electrical circuits and equipment.

Electrical shock has been a recognizable electrical hazard for many years. Yet this hazard is often taken too lightly and remains a tremendous problem in the electrical industry. The human body, while very adaptable, is not designed to handle even the most minimal of electrical currents.

Objectives

» Understand the impact of current on the human body.

» Describe the importance of maintaining and providing adequate protection levels against electrical shock.

» Recognize the relationship between current level and time of duration in current flow and the human body.

More information available in NJATC Blended Learning: Personal Protective Grounding.

For additional information, visit qr.njatcdb.org Item #1823

Chapter 3

Table of Contents

UNDERSTANDING BODY CURRENTS

To understand how much protection is needed, a worker should have an understanding of the permissible amount of current flowing through the body and the potential result if this amount is exceeded.

It is current flow through the body that causes the damage, not the voltage. Voltage only causes the current flow. The amount of body current depends upon both the voltage developed across the body and the resistance of the body, which varies considerably. For example, the dry, calloused hands of a line worker have higher resistance than the softer hands of an office worker. The material the worker's gloves are made of and the type of boots worn both affect the resistance. The value may vary between a few ohms and several thousand ohms. But when contact is made with a line carrying 1,000 volts or more, the outer skin can be punctured, allowing a much higher current to flow through the moist inner-body tissue. Tissue burns and organ damage often result.

A correlation exists with respect to the current level and the time for which the current flows. This means that the body can pass a higher current for a shorter time or a lower current for a longer time and avoid heart fibrillation. Thus, the worker should have an understanding of the operation time of the line protective equipment (how fast the fuse or breaker operates). **See Figure 3-1**.

High Body Currents

A high body current requires sufficient voltage to puncture skin. It also causes heat and burning in body tissues and organs. The severity of the injury is typically determined from complications that occur, and death usually is not immediate.

Today's literature often assumes a body resistance of 1,000 ohms. While this is only an approximate value, it allows calculations and comparisons to be made among safety equipment offerings. The most serious current path is from hand to hand and involves the chest cavity. The path of hand to foot may or may not be less dangerous. Although a shock may be painful rather than fatal, it may still cause a related accident. In other words, a shock reaction may not be fatal, but it could cause a loss of balance, a fall, or the dropping of equipment. **See Figure 3-2**.

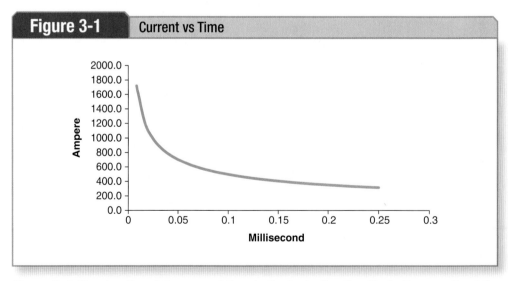

Figure 3-1. The duration of the current flow in the body directly affects the severity of the electrical shock.

For additional information, visit qr.njatcdb.org Item #1823

Figure 3-2   Current Pathways Through the Human Body

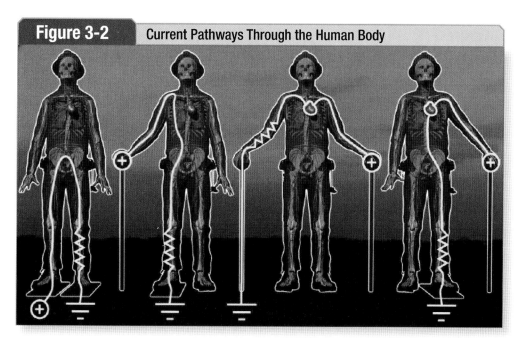

Figure 3-2. The pathway that the current takes in the human body directly affects the severity of the electrical shock. More information available in NJATC Blended Learning: Personal Protective Grounding.

The protection methods are designed to ensure that the body voltage is maintained below a selected safe level. It must be reduced from the high current level that results in burns or serious injury to a level below that of heart fibrillation. This is a difficult task, but it is achievable in most cases.

Threshold Currents

Before the risk of heart fibrillation is reached, there are two important threshold currents that are ideally avoided: perception current and let-go current.

Perception Current. A perception current is the lowest current that the average person can detect with his or her hand. With this threshold current, there is a slight tingling in the hand. For the average male worker, this occurs at 0.0011 amperes, or 1.1 milliamperes. The threshold is lower for the average female worker.

Let-Go Current. At the let-go current, pain is caused with loss of voluntary muscle control. At the threshold current, muscles contract and a hand grip on an energized object cannot be released. Suffocation can occur if the current flow is through the chest. The heart and lungs also may stop functioning. For males, the let-go threshold current is 0.016 amperes or 16 milliamperes; for women, this threshold current is 0.0105 amperes, or 10.5 milliamperes.

Heart Fibrillation

When heart fibrillation occurs, the heart "flutters" without pumping blood. The severity of the injury depends on the elapsed time of fibrillation, and there is a limited window within which to treat the injury before death.

To return the heart to a rhythmic beat, defibrillation is required. Although standard on ambulances, an automated external defibrillator (AED) is becoming more common on construction line crews. Thus, basic first-aid care should be given until an ambulance carrying the device arrives.

Figure 3-3 | Dalziel's Testing

Figure 3-3. Dalziel performed low-current tests on student volunteers to evaluate how their bodies reacted.

CHARLES DALZIEL'S RESEARCH

Charles Dalziel, a professor of electrical engineering at the University of California at Berkeley, made low-current tests in the 1950s and 1960s to evaluate the body's reaction and then calculated them to higher current levels. The tests were conducted on college student volunteers. **See Figure 3-3.**

A formula was developed from the research. It provides the basis for the charts typically used by utility safety departments. The formula is:

$$I = \frac{k}{\sqrt{t}}$$

where I is the current in milliamperes, k is a function of shock energy, and t is time in seconds. Here, k is an empirical constant based on the worker's weight. For example, k_{50} for a body weight of 110 pounds (50 kilograms) is 116, and k_{70} for a body weight of 155 pounds (70 kilograms) is 157.

The protection sought by this formula is to avoid heart fibrillation. As mentioned earlier, fibrillation occurs when the heart's rhythmic beating stops and is replaced by a fluttering action. If the current is held below the level calculated by this formula, 99.5% of workers will not go into heart fibrillation.

Dalziel used a safer low current during the actual tests. The resulting data were extrapolated to high-current values. **See Figure 3-4.**

Figure 3-4 Current Levels and the Average Person		
Effect	**Men**	**Women**
	(ampere)	
No sensation on the hand	0.0004	0.0003
Slight tingling (perception threshold)	0.0011	0.0007
Shock, not painful; muscle control not lost	0.0018	0.0012
Painful shock; muscle control not lost	0.0090	0.0060
Painful shock (let-go threshold)	0.016	0.0105
Painful and severe shock; muscles contract, breathing difficult	0.023	0.015
Possible ventricular fibrillation		
From short shocks (0.03 seconds)	1	1
From longer shocks (3.0 seconds)	0.1	0.1
Ventricular fibrillation, certain death	Must occur during susceptible phase of heart cycle to be lethal.	
From short shocks (0.03 seconds)	2.75	2.75
From short shocks (3.0 seconds)	0.275	0.275

Figure 3-4. Research has determined the current levels an average person can detect or withstand. The "average" body cannot necessarily be applied to all individuals.

Summary

Charles Dalziel, who tested the body's reaction to currents in the mid-1900s, found that a male worker should be protected against current to a perception level (the least amount of current detectable by the ungloved hand) of 1.1 milliamperes. The protection level for shock that is painful but during which muscle control is not lost is 9 milliamperes for the average male. The painful shock, or let-go, threshold for the average man is 16 milliamperes.

When heart fibrillation occurs, the heart "flutters" without pumping blood. Possible ventricular fibrillation occurs at more than 1,000 milliamperes with a duration of 0.030 seconds and more than 100 milliamperes with a duration of 0.300 seconds. The body may pass a higher current for a shorter time or a lower current for a longer time and avoid heart fibrillation.

Review Questions

1. The most serious body current path is from __?__.
   a. foot to foot
   b. hand to foot
   c. hand to hand
   d. hip to foot

2. At the let-go current threshold of __?__, the muscles of a male contract and a hand grip on an energized object cannot be released. For women, this threshold current is 10.5 milliamperes.
   a. 8 mA
   b. 12 mA
   c. 16 mA
   d. 20 mA

3. Studies have determined that both males and females can suffer ventricular fibrillation from longer shocks (3.0 seconds) with body current levels as low as __?__.
   a. 0.1 A
   b. 0.3 A
   c. 0.5 A
   d. 0.7 A

4. Low-current tests to evaluate the body's reaction were conducted on college student volunteers by __?__.
   a. Abraham Maslow
   b. Charles Dalziel
   c. Heinrich Lenz
   d. Nikola Tesla

5. An average male will sustain a painful shock without muscle control loss at a current of 9 milliamperes. A current of __?__ will have the same effect on a female.
   a. 4 mA
   b. 6 mA
   c. 8 mA
   d. 10 mA

Basic Electricity and Circuits

Working safely on the job site is a multifaceted task. Performing the proper task or work practice in the correct order is only one part of working safely. Worker safety can be greatly enhanced by having and using fundamental knowledge of electrical theory and design. This is particularly apparent when studying Ohm's Law.

This theory not only provides a framework for understanding electrical circuits but also for how to provide protection on the job site. For example, the laws of current flow and division in a parallel circuit provide a basis for the personal protective grounding scheme.

Objectives

» Understand series circuit principles as they relate to Ohm's Law.

» Understand parallel circuit principles as they relate to Ohm's Law.

» Understand combination circuit principles as they relate to Ohm's Law.

» Consider how the placement of a very low-resistance path in parallel with the line worker forms the basis of personal protective grounding.

Chapter 4

Table of Contents

THE RELATIONSHIP BETWEEN OHM'S LAW AND BASIC CIRCUITS

Often a line worker can master a job task without a complete understanding of some of the details. For example, a cutout can be changed on a deenergized line without understanding electricity. But this is not always the case when applying personal protective grounding. A basic understanding of electricity is needed in case an unusual situation arises and the "tried and true" predefined method does not provide the needed protection.

Only simple arithmetic—addition, subtraction, multiplication, or division—is needed to apply Ohm's Law. This law is a simple relationship between voltage, current, and resistance. If two are known, the third (or the unknown) can be calculated.

Thus, according to Ohm's Law,

$$E = I \times R \quad \text{or} \quad I = \frac{E}{R} \quad \text{or} \quad R = \frac{E}{I}$$

where E is the voltage in volts, I is the current in amperes, and R is the resistance in ohms, which is usually represented by the Greek letter omega (Ω).

BASIC CIRCUITS

To understand grounding, a worker must have working knowledge of basic circuits. Electrical circuits are connected in series configurations, parallel configurations, or a combination of both. The following five circuits are supplied by a 120 volt AC source. The resistors are lamps connected in series, parallel, or combination circuits. Although the voltage, current, and resistance values differ from what is found on distribution and transmission systems, these same laws and principles apply to power line circuits.

Series Circuits

All current flows though one continuous path. This is the essence of a series circuit. **See Figure 4-1.**

As current flows through any resistance, a voltage is developed across the resistance. This is known as voltage drop. Each resistor's voltage drop is a percentage of the total circuit resistance. The sum of all these voltage drops equals the total or source voltage.

$$E_T = E_1 + E_2 + \dots E_N$$

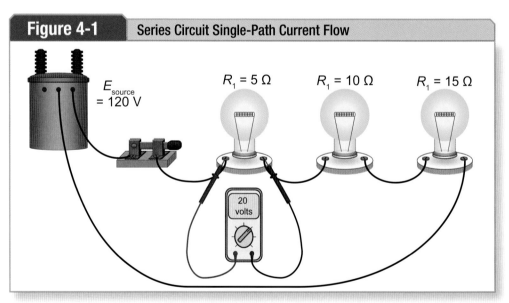

| Figure 4-1 | Series Circuit Single-Path Current Flow |

Figure 4-1. The current flow through a series circuit is the same at all points of the circuit. The same amount of current that flows through the switch also flows through each of the lamp filaments. The total resistance in a series circuit is equal to the sum of the individual resistances. In this circuit, $R_T = 5\,\Omega + 10\,\Omega + 15\,\Omega = 30\,\Omega$.

The total circuit resistance (R_T) is equal to the sum of the individual resistors present in the circuit:

$$R_T = R_1 + R_2 + \ldots R_N,$$

where N is the last resistor of the circuit.

Consider the following example. Here source voltage and load resistances are given (the two known values of Ohm's Law), and the equation is solved for the circuit current (the unknown). Thus the known values are as follows:

$$E = 120 \text{ VAC}$$
$$R_1 = 5 \text{ }\Omega$$
$$R_2 = 10 \text{ }\Omega$$
$$R_3 = 15 \text{ }\Omega$$

Add the given resistances of the three lamps to find the total circuit resistance.

$$R_T = 5 \text{ }\Omega + 10 \text{ }\Omega + 15 \text{ }\Omega = 30 \text{ }\Omega$$

To solve for the total current flow in the circuit, use the Ohm's Law equation.

$$I_T = \frac{E_{source}}{R_T}$$

Insert the given voltage and found total resistance into the equation and divide.

$$I_T = \frac{120 \text{ volts}}{30 \text{ }\Omega} = 4 \text{ amps}$$

Using the found circuit current, the voltage drop across each of the lamps can be found using the Ohm's Law formula, $E = I \times R$.

The voltage drop across each lamp is:

$$\begin{aligned} E_{R_1} &= I_{R_1} \times R_1 \\ &= 4 \text{ amps} \times 5 \text{ }\Omega \\ &= 20 \text{ volts} \end{aligned}$$

$$\begin{aligned} E_{R_2} &= I_{R_2} \times R_2 \\ &= 4 \text{ amps} \times 10 \text{ }\Omega \\ &= 40 \text{ volts} \end{aligned}$$

$$\begin{aligned} E_{R_3} &= I_{R_3} \times R_3 \\ &= 4 \text{ amps} \times 15 \text{ }\Omega \\ &= 60 \text{ volts} \end{aligned}$$

Note that the lamp with the highest resistance, R_3, has the greatest voltage drop.

Without current flow there is no voltage drop across the resistors. **See Figure 4-2.** The opened switch has interrupted the circuit current flow. As shown, the voltmeter reading is zero across the R_1 lamp terminals. The readings across the R_2 and

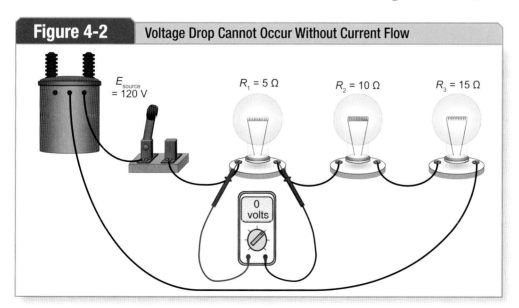

Figure 4-2   **Voltage Drop Cannot Occur Without Current Flow**

Figure 4-2. Current flow through the circuit is interrupted when the switch is opened. Without current flow, there can be no voltage drops across any of the resistors.

R_3 lamps will be zero as well. A reading across the open switch would be 120 volts and equal to the source voltage.

In series circuits and series resistance, two points are crucial to the study of personal protective grounding for worker safety:

1. There is no voltage drop over the resistance without current flow, and
2. For a given current, the circuit component with the highest resistance develops the greatest voltage.

Parallel Circuits

The parallel circuit differs from the series circuit in that the current path separates into multiple paths and then later recombines into a single path. **See Figure 4-3.**

To evaluate a parallel circuit, a knowledge of resistor performance is required. The circuit resistance does not equal the sum, as it did in a series circuit. Resistors in parallel combine as their reciprocals, which is 1/R. For example,

$$\frac{1}{R_{EQ}} = \frac{1}{R_1} + \frac{1}{R_2} + \frac{1}{R_3} + ... \frac{1}{R_N}$$

when N is the last paralleled resistor. R_{EQ} is the value of a single imaginary resistor that could be substituted for an entire parallel group of resistors without changing the electrical properties of the circuit. The resistor equivalent, R_{EQ}, always has a value less than the smallest resistor in the combination.

The voltage drop across R_{EQ} is the same as across the parallel combination it replaces. The current through R_{EQ} is the same as the current through the switch and through the wire return to the transformer.

When only two resistors are being considered, the following product over sum equation can be used to determine R_{EQ}:

$$R_{EQ} = \frac{R_1 \times R_2}{R_1 + R_2}$$

The sum of the currents through the parallel branches is equal to the current both entering and leaving the parallel branches. The 120 volt source voltage and the equivalent resistor value are used to determine the current flow through the circuit. **See Figure 4-3.**

Two steps are required to evaluate a parallel circuit:

1. Determine the value of R_{EQ}. Because there are only two paralleled resistors, the product over sum equation can be used.

$$R_{EQ} = \frac{R_1 \times R_2}{R_1 + R_2} = \frac{30 \times 20}{30 + 20} = \frac{600}{50} = 12\ \Omega$$

2. Use the Ohm's Law equation to calculate the current based on the given source voltage and the found equivalent resistance.

$$I_T = \frac{E_{source}}{R_{EQ}} = \frac{120\ volts}{12\ \Omega} = 10\ amps$$

Because the resistors are connected in parallel, the voltage drop is the same

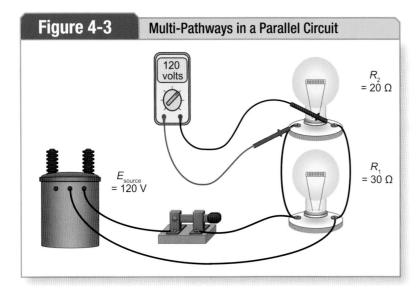

| Figure 4-3 | Multi-Pathways in a Parallel Circuit |

Figure 4-3. *The voltage across parallel circuit branches is equal to the source voltage. The current divides at parallel circuit branch paths and the flow through the branch resistances is in proportion to the resistance value. The total circuit resistance must be found to find the total circuit current. The product over sum method can be used when there are two current paths.*

across each branch resistor. The current through each parallel branch depends upon each resistor's value. The lower the resistance value, the greater the current flow.

Current will flow through every path of a parallel circuit. The same Ohm's Law equation as used to calculate the total circuit current will be used to find the current flow through the individual branches. The voltage across the branches is equal to the source voltage. The voltage is divided by the resistance value of the branch to solve for the current through the branch.

$$I_{R_1} = \frac{E_{R_1}}{R_1} = \frac{120 \text{ volts}}{30 \ \Omega} = 4 \text{ amps}$$

$$I_{R_2} = \frac{E_{R_1}}{R_2} = \frac{120 \text{ volts}}{20 \ \Omega} = 6 \text{ amps}$$

The sum of the currents flowing through the parallel branches is equal to the total circuit current. $I_T = I_1 + I_2$.

The reciprocal equation can be used to find the equivalent resistance of a parallel circuit with any number of resistors. When more than two resistors of various sizes are connected in parallel, it is the method to be used. **See Figure 4-4.**

The reciprocal equation is used to solve for equivalent resistance.

$$\frac{1}{R_{EQ}} = \frac{1}{R_1} + \frac{1}{R_2} + \frac{1}{R_3} + \frac{1}{R_4}$$

Insert the given lamp resistance values.

$$\frac{1}{R_{EQ}} = \frac{1}{10} + \frac{1}{15} + \frac{1}{20} + \frac{1}{30}$$

Find the common denominator, convert the fractions, and then add.

$$\frac{1}{R_{EQ}} = \frac{6}{60} + \frac{4}{60} + \frac{3}{60} + \frac{2}{60} = \frac{15}{60}$$

Therefore:

$$R_{EQ} = \frac{60}{15} = 4 \ \Omega$$

In any parallel circuit, the equivalent resistance is always less than the resistance of the branch with the lowest resistance value.

Using the Ohm's Law equation, the given source voltage, and found equivalent resistance, the total circuit current can be found.

$$I_T = \frac{E_{source}}{R_{EQ}} = \frac{120 \text{ volts}}{4 \ \Omega} = 30 \text{ amps}$$

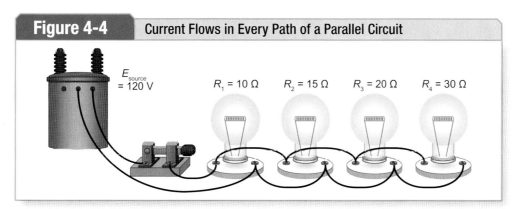

Figure 4-4   Current Flows in Every Path of a Parallel Circuit

$E_{source} = 120 \text{ V}$ $R_1 = 10 \ \Omega$ $R_2 = 15 \ \Omega$ $R_3 = 20 \ \Omega$ $R_4 = 30 \ \Omega$

Figure 4-4. The current divides and flows through every branch of this circuit. The total circuit current can be calculated only after the equivalent resistance is found. The reciprocal method is used to solve for the equivalent resistance in a parallel circuit with more than two resistors.

Ohm's Law is used to solve for the current through each of the lamp resistors.

$$I_{R_1} = \frac{E_{R_1}}{R_1} = \frac{120 \text{ volts}}{10 \ \Omega} = 12 \text{ amps}$$

$$I_{R_2} = \frac{E_{R_2}}{R_2} = \frac{120 \text{ volts}}{15 \ \Omega} = 8 \text{ amps}$$

$$I_{R_3} = \frac{E_{R_3}}{R_3} = \frac{120 \text{ volts}}{20 \ \Omega} = 6 \text{ amps}$$

$$I_{R_4} = \frac{E_{R_4}}{R_4} = \frac{120 \text{ volts}}{30 \ \Omega} = 4 \text{ amps}$$

Note that the lamp with the lowest resistance, R_1, has the highest current flow.

In a parallel circuit, the total current is equal to the sum of the branch currents.

$$I_T = I_{R_1} + I_{R_2} + I_{R_3} + I_{R_4}$$

Series/Parallel Circuits

In a series/parallel or combination circuit there are resistors connected in series and also resistors grouped in parallel. **See Figure 4-5.** Using Ohm's Law, follow the step by step instructions to solve for the total and individual resistor currents and voltage drops.

1. Begin by reducing the parallel branches, R_3 and R_4, to an equivalent resistance. Because there are two branches in the parallel part of the circuit, the product over sum method can be used.

$$R_{3,4EQ} = \frac{R_3 \times R_4}{R_3 + R_4} = \frac{10 \times 15}{10 + 15} = \frac{150}{25} = 6 \ \Omega$$

2. The $R_{3,4}$ equivalent resistance can be considered a single resistor in series with the R_1 and R_2 resistors. The total circuit resistance is found by adding the individual series connected resistances.

$$R_T = R_1 + R_2 + R_{3,4EQ} = 6 + 12 + 6 = 24 \ \Omega$$

3. The total circuit current is found dividing the source voltage by the total resistance.

$$I_T = \frac{E_{source}}{R_T} = \frac{120 \text{ volts}}{24 \ \Omega} = 5 \text{ amps}$$

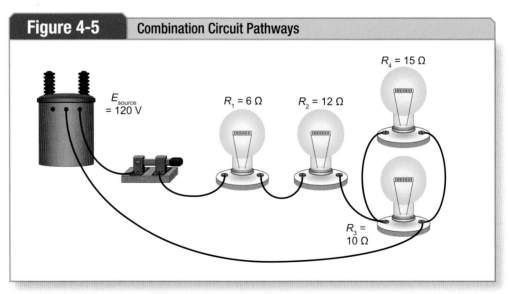

Figure 4-5	Combination Circuit Pathways

$R_4 = 15 \ \Omega$

$E_{source} = 120 \text{ V}$

$R_1 = 6 \ \Omega$ $R_2 = 12 \ \Omega$

$R_3 = 10 \ \Omega$

Figure 4-5. *The total circuit current must flow through the switch, lamp R_1, and lamp R_2. These lamps are resistors in the series portion of this circuit. The current divides across lamps R_3 and R_4; therefore, these resistances are paralleled.*

4. The voltage drops across the series lamps, R_1 and R_2, are found by multiplying the current and resistor value.

$$E_{R_1} = I_{R_1} \times R_1 = 5 \text{ amps} \times 6\ \Omega = 30 \text{ volts}$$
$$E_{R_2} = I_{R_2} \times R_2 = 5 \text{ amps} \times 12\ \Omega = 60 \text{ volts}$$

Because lamps R_3 and R_4 are paralleled, the equivalent resistance value is used in the Ohm's Law equation to solve for the voltage drop across the lamps. The parallel parts of combination circuits always have equal voltage drops across the branches.

$$E_{R_{3,4}} = I_{R_{3,4}} \times R_{3,4}$$
$$= 5 \text{ amps} \times 6\ \Omega = 30 \text{ volts}$$

The sum of the voltage drops is equal to the source voltage.

$$E_{source} = E_{R_1} + E_{R_2} = E_{R_{3,4}}$$
$$= 30 + 60 + 30 = 120 \text{ volts}$$

5. The total circuit current of 5 amps is divided across the paralleled R_3 and R_4 lamps. To find the current through these individual branches, divide the voltage drop by the branch resistances.

$$I_{R_3} = \frac{E_{R_3}}{R_3} = \frac{30 \text{ volts}}{10\ \Omega} = 3 \text{ amps}$$
$$I_{R_4} = \frac{E_{R_4}}{R_4} = \frac{30 \text{ volts}}{15\ \Omega} = 2 \text{ amps}$$

The transmission, distribution, and substation systems owned by utility companies are a complex arrangement of combination circuits. Even the smallest sub-circuits of the electrical grid contain series and parallel resistances. **See Figure 4-6.** The primary supply lines are good conductors, but have resistive properties that oppose current flow. The fused disconnect switches are overcurrent protective devices that are connected in series with the transformer primary

Figure 4-6   Utility Combination Circuits

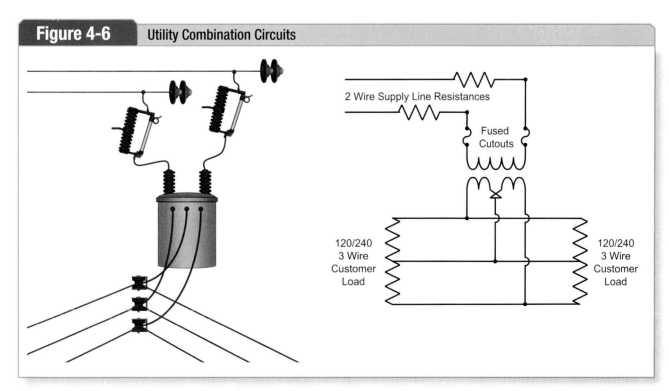

Figure 4-6. The primary supply lines, fused cutouts, leads, and transformer primary coil are elements of a series circuit. The current flow from each of the transformer secondary leads divides at the customer service connections. The secondary lines and customer loads are parallel circuit branches.

winding. The primary coil of the transformer is magnetically coupled to the secondary coils. The transformer secondary leads connect to the customer service lines at which point the current divides. The customer service lines and loads are parallel circuit branches.

An understanding of combination circuit voltage drops and current paths are necessary for the proper selection and application of grounding jumpers and equipment. An analysis of a properly grounded single phase line will prove the effectiveness of the equipotential zone method. The following is an example of

how combination circuit currents and voltage drops apply to temporary grounding and fault current situations. **See Figure 4-7.**

A line worker is investigating an out-of-power call from a rural customer. A blown fuse is discovered where a single phase tap takes off from the main line. Without removing the cutout gate or following the tag-out procedure, the worker patrols the line and discovers a broken insulator. Without returning to the tap source, the worker chooses to test the line, apply temporary grounds, and make the simple repair. The work site is located five miles

Figure 4-7 | Combination Circuit Grounding Scheme

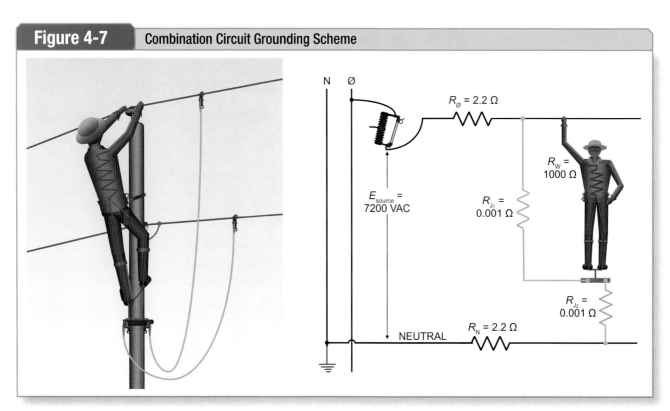

Figure 4-7. If a line is accidentally energized, fault current will flow through a series/parallel circuit. The series components in the circuit include the primary phase conductor ($R_\emptyset$), the cluster bar to neutral grounding jumper (R_{J_2}), and the neutral conductor (R_N). The worker (R_W) and the phase to cluster bar grounding jumper (R_{J_1}) are parallel circuit branches.

from the tap take off. A grounding cluster bar is pole mounted below the worker's pole position and grounding jumpers are connected from the bar to both the phase and the neutral conductors.

While the repair is underway, other workers discover the blown fuse, replace it, and close the cutout to test the line. At the moment the line becomes energized, the person replacing the insulator is in contact with the phase conductor. Fault currents will flow through the combination circuit resistances until the fuse clears the fault. The total clearing time includes the fuse link melt time and the time for the resulting arc to be extinguished.

To total circuit resistance must be found before currents and voltage drops can be calculated. The phase, neutral, and the cluster bar to neutral jumper are series circuit resistances. The phase and neutral conductors are 2/0 American Wire Gauge (AWG) aluminum conductor-steel reinforced. These conductors, $R_\emptyset$ and R_N, are five miles long and each has a resistance of 2.2 ohms. The grounding jumper, R_{J_2}, has a resistance of 0.001 ohms. The worker, R_W, and the phase to cluster bar jumper, R_{J_1}, are parallel circuit branches. Follow the steps to analyze the circuit:

1. Begin by using the product over sum equation to solve for the equivalent resistance of the parallel branches.

$$R_{W,J_{1EQ}} = \frac{R_W \times R_{J_1}}{R_W + R_{J_1}} = \frac{1,000 \times 0.001}{1,000 + 0.001}$$
$$= 0.001\,\Omega \text{ (rounded)}$$

2. Calculate the total circuit resistance by adding the series resistances and the parallel branch equivalent resistance.

$$R_T = R_\emptyset + R_N + R_{J_2} + R_{W,J_{1EQ}}$$
$$R_T = 2.2 + 2.2 + 0.001 + 0.001 = 4.402\,\Omega$$

3. The total circuit current is calculated by dividing the source voltage by the total circuit resistance.

$$I_T = \frac{E_{source}}{R_T} = \frac{7,200 \text{ volts}}{4.402\,\Omega} = 1,636 \text{ amps}$$

4. Calculate the voltage available at the worksite across the R_W and R_{J_1} parallel branches by multiplying the $R_{W,J1}$ equivalent resistance by the available fault current

$$E_{RW,J_1} = I_T \times R_{EQ}$$
$$= 1636 \text{ amps} \times 0.001\,\Omega$$
$$= 1.636 \text{ volt drop across worker and jumper } R_{J_1}$$

5. The current through the individual parallel branches, R_W and R_{J_1}, is calculated by dividing the voltage drop by the branch resistance.

Bypass Jumper Current
$$I_{RJ_1} = \frac{E_{RJ_1}}{R_{J_1}} = \frac{1.636 \text{ volts}}{0.001\,\Omega} = 1,636 \text{ amps}$$

Worker Body Current
$$I_{RW} = \frac{E_W}{R_W} = \frac{1.636 \text{ volts}}{1,000\,\Omega} = 0.001636 \text{ amps}$$

The low-resistance bypass jumper has carried almost all of the fault current while the body current through the worker produces only a slight tingling or non-painful shock. Placing a very low resistance path in parallel with the worker is the principle of equipotential personal protective grounding.

Summary

In any utility transmission or distribution circuit, a combination of series and parallel circuits is almost always found. All current flows through one continuous path in a series circuit. Resistors in series add together into the total circuit resistance. As current flows through any resistance, a voltage is developed, or drops, across the resistance. There must be current flow in a circuit to develop a voltage drop, and the highest resistance develops the highest voltage drop for a given current. The sum of the voltage drops in a series circuit is equal to the source voltage.

The parallel circuit is the basis of equipotential personal protective grounding. In a parallel circuit, some current goes through every possible path, and the resistance in each path determines the amount of current that flows in that path. When two parallel circuits are used together, the sum of the current entering a parallel combination equals that leaving the combination. The voltage across a parallel resistor combination puts the same voltage on each resistor.

Review Questions

1. The formula $R_T = R_1 + R_2 + R_3 + \dots R_N$ is used to solve for the resistance total in __?__ circuits.

    a. all

    b. grounding

    c. parallel

    d. series

2. Voltage is dropped across each resistor in a series circuit. The resistor with the highest ohm value will have __?__.

    a. a voltage drop equal to that of every resistor

    b. a voltage drop equal to the source voltage

    c. the greatest voltage drop

    d. the least voltage drop

3. The R_{EQ} value in a parallel circuit is always __?__ resistor value.

    a. equal to the average

    b. equal to the smallest

    c. greater than the largest

    d. less than the smallest

4. A parallel circuit has two branches with resistances of 4 ohms and 6 ohms. The equivalent resistance of the circuit is __?__.

    a. 2.4 Ω

    b. 3.5 Ω

    c. 5 Ω

    d. 10 Ω

5. The basis of equipotential personal protective grounding is the __?__ circuit.

    a. combination

    b. parallel

    c. series

    d. series/parallel

Equipotential Grounding

An equipotential zone maintains the voltage across the worker to an acceptably low level by placing a low-resistance shunt in parallel with the worker. The basis of this approach is to build on the fundamentals of Ohm's Law. Equipotential grounding is the basic grounding methodology that is preferred for most work situations, and is the most feasible solution for providing worker protection.

Objectives

» Define an equipotential zone.

» Identify equipotential grounding schemes.

» Recognize the advantages to employing equipotential grounding in most worksite applications.

Chapter 5

Table of Contents

EQUIPOTENTIAL ZONES DEFINED

An equipotential zone is a work zone that, by maintaining a low voltage across the worker, keeps the current flow through the worker to an acceptably low level. This is done by placing a low resistance shunt in parallel with the worker. The zones provide a low resistance path for current around the worker and should be used to bypass bodily contact paths (hand to hand, hand to feet, foot to foot). **See Figure 5-1.**

Reminder

Always check local safety rules for PPE when using sticks.

An equipotential configuration offers several improvements over historically used methods. It reduces cable lengths between phases. It also minimizes voltage

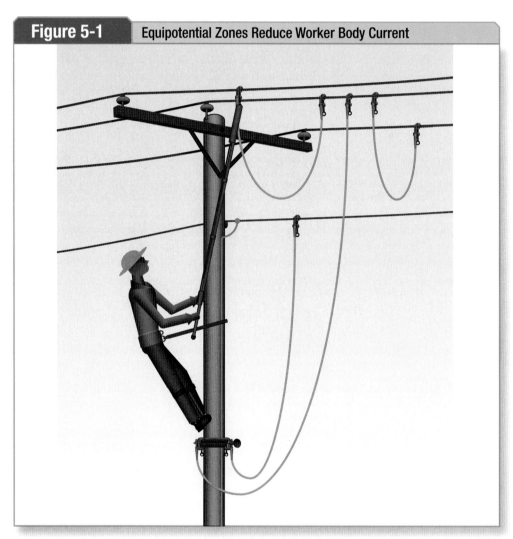

Figure 5-1 | Equipotential Zones Reduce Worker Body Current

Figure 5-1. *The grounding jumper connected to the line and ground cluster bare creates an equipotential zone. The zone includes all surfaces within reach of the worker and is used to reduce the voltage across and thus the body current through the worker.*

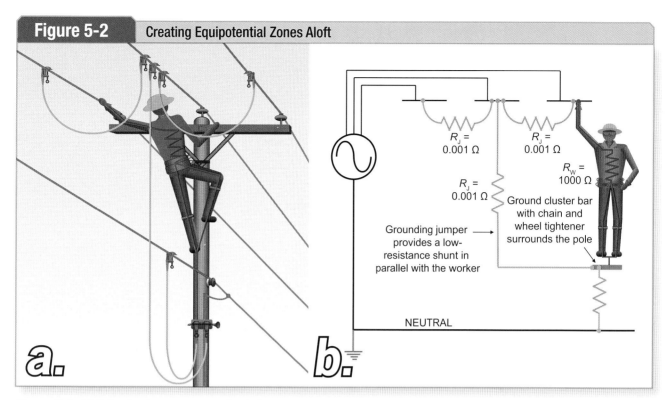

Figure 5-2. (a) If the line becomes energized, there would be a voltage rise on everything above the cluster bar. The grounding cables will conduct heavy fault currents. (b) Because most of the current flow between the lines and the cluster bracket is shunted around the worker, body current flow can be kept to an acceptably low level.

among the conductor, work area, and worker. Finally, with such a configuration, there is minimal voltage drop across the worker in the event of current flow. If a neutral is available, the connection should be made for the lowest resistance to the source.

USES OF EQUIPOTENTIAL ZONES

An equipotential zone can be used in most maintenance tasks, whether the worker is aloft on a wood or a steel structure. It can be used from aerial devices (trucks or lifts), in substations, and by ground workers around structures or aerial devices to avoid both step and touch potential hazards.

When the worker is aloft, the equipotential zone shunts most of the current around the worker. **See Figure 5-2.** This method is required when available.

Reminder

If there is no pole ground present, an additional ground jumper may be attached from the cluster bar to a driven ground rod.

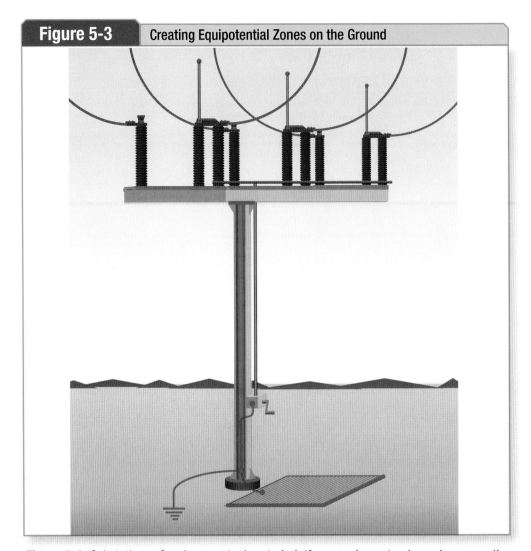

| Figure 5-3 | Creating Equipotential Zones on the Ground |

Figure 5-3. *Substations often have a steel grated platform workers stand on when operating switches. These platforms are permanently bonded to steel support columns that are connected to the substation grid. If an insulator were to flash over during a switching operation, the voltage rise at the handle would be equal to that of the steel platform.*

When the worker is on the ground, the equipotential zone shunts most of the current around the worker. **See Figure 5-3.** This method has long been used in substations and below switch handles.

In all of these cases, suitable equipment must be selected and properly connected.

The equipotential zone limits worker current by using a parallel circuit. This zone also limits worker voltage, which cannot exceed the product of the jumper current and jumper resistance. It does not maintain the same voltage between the hands and the feet. As with current flowing through any resistance, a voltage drop develops. Equipment is selected to ensure that the voltage across the worker is maintained at the desired level. **See Figure 5-4.**

EQUIPOTENTIAL GROUNDING SCHEMES

If equipment is not properly selected and properly connected, a hazard may exist. A false sense of security may lead to an injury or death.

Figure 5-4 | Low-Resistance Jumper

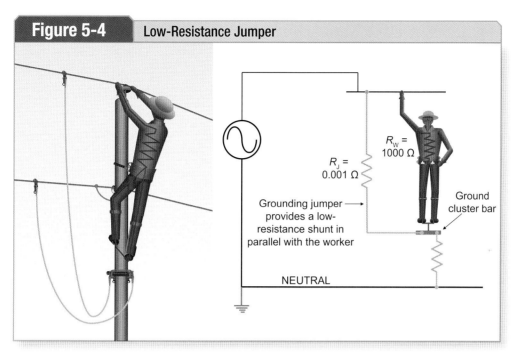

Figure 5-4. The body current path from the worker's hand to the cluster bracket is in parallel with the path through the grounding cable connected from the line to the bracket. When fault current divides in proportion to the branch resistances, most will be shunted through the low-resistance jumper.

Occupational Safety and Health Administration Regulations

The protective connection of an equipotential zone can be used in most situations. However, there are situations in which it cannot be used. Workers must understand the protective principle so that they can make an intelligent choice for an alternate protection method if one is required.

Equipotential protection is a proven method. For example, several Puget Sound Power and Light (P&L) tests conducted in 1987 showed the effectiveness of a personal equipotential ground. First, a single-phase test line was constructed per Puget Sound P&L standards. It was 7.2 kilovolts, with 6 kiloamperes available. The line was built in 300-foot spans with and without pole grounds. The test showed that if no jumpers were used under these conditions, a worker contacting the ground would experience 1,745 volts, a fatal level. A worker on a pole without ground would be hit with

Figure 5-5 | Equipotential Zones Proven Method

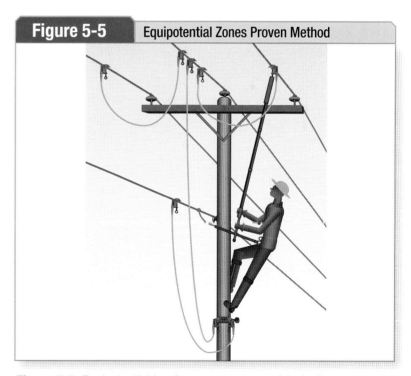

Figure 5-5. Equipotential has been proven to provide the best protection for those working on de-energized isolated likes. This grounding method required by the CFR 1910.269(n)(3) OSHA law applies not only to those working aloft, but to all employees on a job site.

397 volts and 0.326 amperes, which is still fatal.

Better results were obtained when using bracket grounds. In this test, the voltage was 103 volts and the current was 0.095 amperes without a pole ground. With a pole ground, these numbers were 50 volts and 0.054 amperes, although they were site specific in the test.

Still, the best results were obtained with a personal equipotential ground. With or without a pole ground, the worker would experience 22 volts and 24 milliamperes. Therefore, this is the safe method.

Because equipotential protection has proved effective in most situations, its use is enforced by U.S. law. On October 30, 1987, executive order No. 12612 was issued, requesting the development of regulations and new requirements to ensure the safety of electrical workers. Six years of hearings from interested parties followed the executive order. The result was OSHA 29 Code of Federal Regulation (CFR) 1910.269 Subpart R. It was published in the Federal Register on January 31, 1994. This CFR covers generation, transmission, distribution, and tree trimming. The regulation specifies use of an equipotential zone and protective grounding equipment. It also provides rules for testing, order of connection, and order of removal. **See Figure 5-5.**

OSHA regulations specifically cover grounding for the protection of employees, as illustrated by these extracts from the CFR:

OSHA 29 CFR 1926.962 Subpart V focuses on grounding regulations during construction, setting the same rules as in OSHA 29 CFR 1910.269. Deenergization will be required per OSHA 29 CFR 1926.961 upon final approval. Both an equipotential zone and line testing are required. Finally, order of placement and order of removal are specified.

Configuring Equipotential Grounding Schemes

The connection in equipotential grounding is a repeat of that in parallel circuits.

The low-resistance jumper placed in parallel with the worker is what offers the protection. A jumper is a conductor placed across the clear space between the ends of two conductors or metal pulling lines. These ends are spliced together to act as a shunt capable of carrying continuous current. This prevents workers from accidentally placing themselves in series between the two conductors.

| Figure 5-6 | Guy Wire Bonding |

Figure 5-6. Structures supporting distribution circuits often have guy wires installed without the attachment hardware bonded or grounded. Sometimes these guy wires are installed without the insulating link that provides an electrical separation between the upper guy components and earth. A worker aloft is at risk if in contact with the guy wire and any conductor during energization or if induction is present. A grounding jumper bonding the guy wire to the cluster bar or the neutral makes the entire guy wire assembly a part of the equipotential zone.

Temporary protective grounds shall be placed at such locations and arranged in such a manner as to prevent each employee from being exposed to hazardous difference in electrical potential. **(OSHA 29 CFR 1910.269(n)(3))**

Protective grounding equipment shall be capable of conducting the maximum fault current that could flow at the point of grounding for the time necessary to clear the fault. This equipment shall have an ampacity greater than or equal to that of No. 2 AWG copper.... Protective grounds shall have an impedance low enough to cause immediate operation of the protective devices in case of accidental energizing of the lines or equipment. **(OSHA 29 CFR 1910.269(n)(4)(i)–(ii))**

Any current divides between the worker and the personal protective jumper in proportion to the resistance of the paths. The maximum allowable voltage across the worker must be considered when selecting the equipment, as well as the available current.

One hazard in the area is the pole guys. The connections from a structure ground wire to hardware and from hardware to an overhead ground wire and guy wires are bolted connections. These are not necessarily good electrical connections. Overhead ground wire connections should be inspected during the installation of grounding cables to ensure adequate worker protection. Guy wires should not be used for personal protective grounding wire attachment.

Pole guys are usually connected directly to an earth anchor. Without current flow in them, they are held to 0 volts. At an elevated worksite, they may be close to the worker, who can form a bridge between a conductor or neutral and the guy wires. If a fault occurs or induction is present, the worker may be injured. **See Figure 5-6.**

Summary

Only three methods protect workers: isolation, insulation, and equipotential zones. Equipotential zones maintain an acceptable level of voltage across the worker (or an acceptable level of current through the body). They provide a low resistance path for current around the worker and should be used to bypass bodily contact paths (hand to hand, hand to feet, and foot to foot). Equipotential grounding is required by U.S. law in most work situations.

Review Questions

1. **On wooden poles, equipotential zones limit the body currents through workers by shunting fault currents around the workers through the __?__.**
    a.   neutral lines
    b.   personal jumpers and cluster bars
    c.   phase to phase grounding jumpers
    d.   temporary ground rods

2. **OSHA 29 CFR 1910.269 states that grounding equipment shall have an ampacity greater than or equal to that of __?__.**
    a.   Number 4 AWG copper
    b.   Number 2 AWG copper
    c.   1/0 copper
    d.   2/0 aluminum

3. **If available, the lowest resistance return path to the source is the __?__.**
    a.   earth
    b.   neutral
    c.   overhead shield wire
    d.   pole ground wire

4. **OSHA 29 CFR 1926.962 SUBPART V grounding regulations during construction are unlike the grounding laws in OSHA 29 CFR 1910.269.**
    a.   True
    b.   False

5. **Any current divides between the worker and the personal protective jumper in proportion to the resistance of the paths. If an available fault current of 5,000 amperes is divided by a 0.001 ohms jumper and a 1,000 ohms worker, the body current through the worker is __?__.**
    a.   0.005 A (or 5 mA)
    b.   0.05 A (or 50 mA)
    c.   0.5 A (or 500 mA)
    d.   5 A

Selection of Equipment

Because equipotential grounding is the only acceptable means for achieving personal protective grounding, it is important to understand the process of selecting proper equipment to accomplish this grounding. There are three basic steps or pieces of information that must be obtained to properly select adequate personal protective grounding equipment. In addition to the selection of the equipment, the placement of equipment such as jumper sets, can significantly affect the overall level of safety of the grounding scheme.

Objectives

» Size the personal protective grounding equipment to carry the maximum available fault current for the maximum time it may flow without fusing.

» Select personal protective grounding equipment to meet the required worker body current and voltage specifications.

» Place the personal protective grounding assemblies to minimize the total resistance in parallel with the worker.

Chapter 6

Table of Contents

EQUIPMENT SELECTION VARIABLES

While accidental reenergizing of deenergized lines can occur, it is probably not the most common cause of accidents. However, because it can happen, the grounding equipment must be sized and selected to carry the maximum fault current that can be available at every worksite where a worker may be present.

The allowable voltage developed across the worker must also be defined. The last item needed is the operation timing of the circuit protective equipment. The body can pass a higher current for a shorter time or a lower current for a longer time for the same avoidance of heart fibrillation.

When selecting the necessary personal protective grounding equipment, it is important to choose that equipment based on the variables involved in the project. It is the responsibility of the utility or employer to define the variables involved. These variables must be evaluated, and then the equipment limitations must be chosen to meet the requirements. Finally, suitable equipment can be selected. It must meet the following requirements:

- Current versus time
- Maximum resistance
- Maximum body voltage or current

Three initial steps for selection are involved. They relate to work area, body current, and fault current:

1. The utility or employer must define the work area where the equipment will be used and the maximum fault current level available in that area.
2. The utility or employer must define the maximum allowable body voltage drop (or put another way, the maximum body current of the worker).
3. The utility or employer must define the maximum time it will take the line protectors to clear the circuit of voltage, which defines the maximum time the fault current can flow (also referred to as the breaker opening times).

A worker is not normally expected to have complete knowledge of these definitions.

HARDWARE REQUIREMENTS

A personal protective ground assembly consists of a cable, two clamps, and two crimp ferrules.

A complete pole-type ground set includes preassembled jumpers with clamps and ferrules. **See Figure 6-1.**

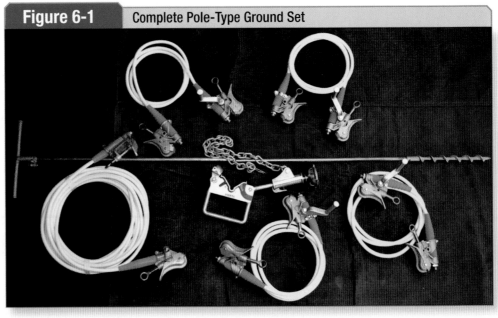

| Figure 6-1 | Complete Pole-Type Ground Set |

Figure 6-1. A complete grounding set may consist of grounding jumper assemblies with duck-bill conductor clamps, a temporary screw-in ground rod, and a cluster bar.

When it comes to hardware require-ments, clamps must be mechanically strong, have low resistance, and be easily installed. Ferrules also must have low resis-tance, which requires tight connections.

Clamps

Ground clamps are selected in accor-dance with American Society for Testing and Materials (ASTM) Standard F855. They have seven current-carrying rat-ings. Ground clamps are assigned the same rating as that of the grounding cable and are sized to meet or exceed the cur-rent-carrying capacity of the cable. They are designed to provide a strong mechan-ical connection to the conductor, metal structure, or ground wire or rod. By design the weakest part of the assembly is the cable, because so much research and testing has been done on the cable. Designing and testing clamps and fer-rules to make sure the cable is the weak point ensures that the remaining parts meet or exceed the cable rating.

ASTM clamps come in many body styles and are normally made of bronze or aluminum alloys. When choosing ground clamps, the following variables should be considered:

- What is the clamp type (C type, duckbill, flat face, or tower)?
- What is the fault current capacity?
- Does the clamp have an eye screw or T-handle and an Acme or V thread?
- What is the body made of: alumi-num or bronze?
- Are the jaws serrated or smooth?
- Are the terminals threaded or plain?

The clamp selected should be chosen to meet the requirements of the work. Weight and ease of use are necessary consider-ations. The final selection of equipment is a matter of worker preference, providing it meets all requirements.

Grounding clamps are manufactured in four main types, according to their func-tion and methods of installation. The first are Type I clamps, which are installed to electrically isolate normally energized conductors. They are equipped with eyes for installation with removable hot sticks.

The C-type ground clamp is a Type I clamp used on a range of conductor and

tubular buses. **See Figure 6-2.** Versions are available with serrated or smooth jaws. The serrated jaws are better able to penetrate corrosion, and can provide a lower-resistance connection.

Duckbill ground clamps are also among the Type I options. **See Figure 6-3.** They

Figure 6-2 C-Type Ground Clamp

Figure 6-2. C-type ground clamps can be used on a variety of conductors and buses.

Figure 6-3 Duckbill Ground Clamps

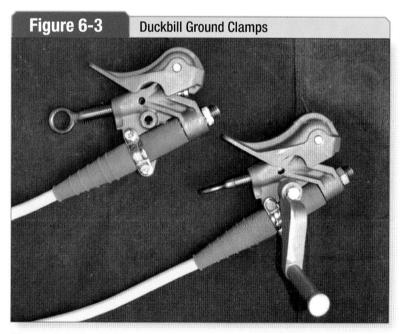

Figure 6-3. Duckbill ground clamps feature springloaded duckbills and have various sized grip ranges.

Figure 6-4 — Flat-Face Ground Clamps

Figure 6-4. Flat-face clamps are designed for attachment to flat surfaces like beam flanges. These types of clamps are also available with eye screws in place of the T handles.

Figure 6-5 — Ball-and-Socket Ground Clamps

Figure 6-5. The ball-and-socket design allows the clamp to be installed over a range of angles.

Figure 6-6 — Studs for Ball-and-Socket Ground Clamps

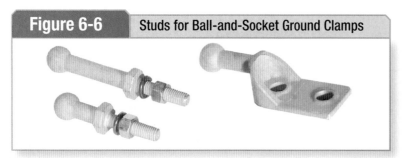

Figure 6-6. Ball-and-socket studs are designed to a specific ball size and shape.

Figure 6-7 — Tower Ground Clamps

Figure 6-7. Tower ground clamps are solely used on steel towers.

are designed for quick installation on a range of conductors. The large spring-loaded duckbill allows for easy installation. They are rated up to ASTM Grade 5 (43 kiloamperes at 15 cycles).

The second group consists of Type III clamps, designed for installation on permanently grounded conductors or metal structures. They have T-handles, eyes, square or hexagon head screws, or a combination of these. The flat-face ground clamp is one such Type III clamp. **See Figure 6-4.** It is designed for connection to flat surfaces and uses a set screw to assist in the mechanical connection.

For example, a typical grounding cable for transmission line work consists of a 2/0 American Wire Gauge (AWG) copper cable with an insulating jacket. It is equipped with an all-angle conductor clamp at the conductor end and a flat-face clamp with a set screw at the ground end.

Ball-and-socket is the third type of clamp. Ball-and-socket ground clamps have a unique design ideal for substations, switchgear, and industrial applications. This design permits installation at various angles. These clamps are only used on a ball of the size and shape designed for the specific socket-type clamp. These clamps are available with an eye screw or T-handle. They are rated up to grade 5 (43 kiloamperes at 15 cycles). **See Figure 6-5.** Ball-and-socket clamps have studs. **See Figure 6-6.**

In the fourth category are other types of special clamps designed for specific applications, such as cluster and underground equipment grounding. For example, tower ground clamps are designed for connection to tower steel angles. **See Figure 6-7.**

Bus clamps should be furnished with smooth jaws for installation on copper, aluminum, or silver-plated bus work without marring the surface. Conductor or metal structure clamps should be furnished with serrations or cross-hatching designed to abrade or bite through corrosion products on the surfaces of the conductor or the metal structure being clamped. Several styles of conductor and ground-end clamps have jaws that can be replaced when the serrations have worn. Serrated jaws are recommended for conductor-end clamps used on aluminum or steel-reinforced conductors. Several styles of ground-end clamps are designed with a cup point set screw, which should be tightened with a wrench (after the serrated jaws have been securely tightened) to break through paint, rust, galvanized coating, or corrosion on the surface that is to be clamped.

Ferrules

Ferrules are designed for crimp connection to cable. They need to carry the same current rating as the cable. It is recommended that ferrules always be used to terminate the jumper cable. **See Figure 6-8.**

Depending on the type of stress relief desired, ferrules can be shrouded or unshrouded. To reduce damage from broken strands, a tight crimped connection and resistance to oxidation are often achieved with the addition of an oxidation inhibitor.

Ferrules can be threaded or plain; the choice is made so that the ferrule style matches the ground clamp terminal. **See Figure 6-9.** Threaded plug-type ferrules are recommended by the ASTM, because clamps are designed for use with threaded stud copper-base compression ferrules. The threaded stud fitting should be checked for tightness periodically. Ferrules are available in aluminum or plated copper. Plated copper ferrules can be used with either aluminum or bronze clamps.

Ferrules should have the filler compound vent hole at the bottom of the cable so that workers can visually check

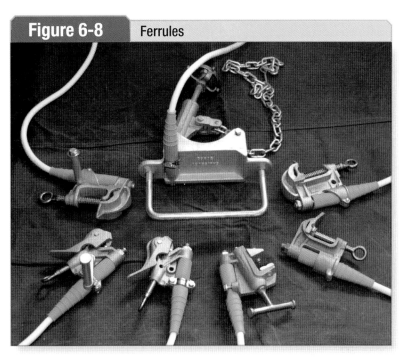

Figure 6-8. Ferrules

Figure 6-8. *Grounding cables may be attached to the grounding equipment with threaded compression ferrules.*

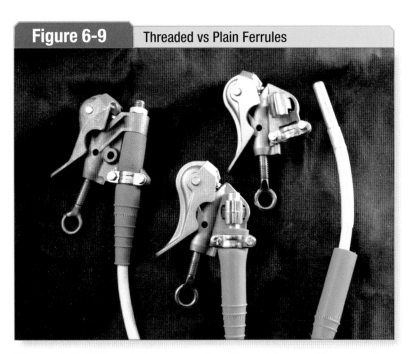

Figure 6-9. Threaded vs Plain Ferrules

Figure 6-9. *Different clamps require different types of ferrules. They may be bored and tapped with a threaded ferrule attached (left) or have a plain ferrule attached with a pressure terminal (center). A disconnected cable (right) shows a clear heat shrink tube installed at the ferrule to cable joint.*

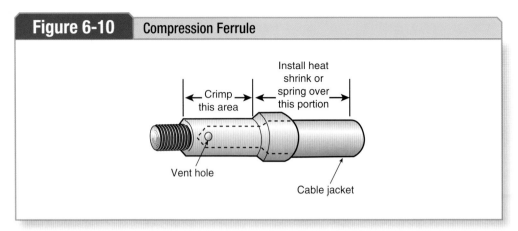

| Figure 6-10 | Compression Ferrule |

Crimp this area

Install heat shrink or spring over this portion

Vent hole

Cable jacket

Figure 6-10. *A compression ferrule is crimped in the narrow portion but not in the wider base where the cable jacket is inserted.*

that the cable is fully inserted into the ferrule. **See Figure 6-10.** The ferrule manufacturers recommend that compound be used with crimped ferrules. The ferrules should be crimped with the

ferrule manufacturer's recommended die. The press has enough pressure to completely close the die. The area covering the inserted cable jacket should not be compressed. Heat shrink, which shrinks as heat is applied, should be installed over a portion of the ferrule to minimize strand breakage caused by bending. In all cases, the manufacturer's recommendations should be followed. Caution should be used if springs are installed, because induction can cause heating and can reduce the cable rating.

The cable-to-ferrule interface should never be limited to a soldered joint. The solder melts and separates under fault conditions, leaving the worker without protection. Solder may only be used to seal an open-end crimp ferrule to reduce the ingress of moisture.

Grounding Jumpers

A grounding jumper assembly has multiple resistances. A jumper resistance consists of both cable resistance and clamp resistance. **See Figure 6-11.** Most of the jumper assembly resistance is found in the contact point, that is, clamp to conductor, clamp to ferrule, and ferrule to cable on each end. **See Figure 6-12.**

When new (with clean and tight connections), the assembly resistance can be on the order of milliohms. However, after extended exposure and use, the contact

| Figure 6-11 | Grounding Jumper |

Conductor

$R_{Surface\ contact\ conductor}$

R_{Clamp}

$R_{Ferrule}$

R_{Cable}

$R_{Ferrule}$

R_{Clamp}

$R_{Surface\ contact}$

Ground rod or neutral wire

Figure 6-11. *The total resistance of a grounding jumper set is the sum of the individual component resistances plus the resistance of the clamp contact surfaces. The resistance of the cable varies with the length and size.*

resistances normally increase due to oxidation, corrosion, and some looseness.

A complete clean and tight jumper set may be as low as 0.0005 ohm. For a safe margin, allow 0.001 ohm per jumper assembly.

Careful correct positioning of the jumpers to the center phase of a 3-phase system limits the number of jumpers in parallel with the worker to two. **See Figure 6-16.**

Reminder

If there is no pole ground present, an additional ground jumper must be attached from the cluster bar to a driven ground rod.

| Figure 6-12 | Field Inspection |

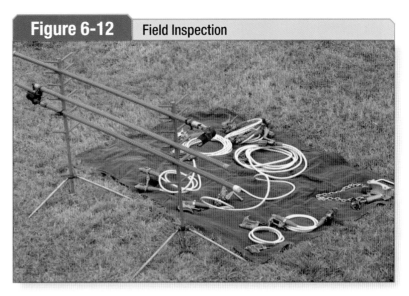

Figure 6-12. *After the proper equipment for the grounding task is selected, and before being installed on the line, each jumper is inspected for damage. Loose ferrule to clamp connections, broken wire connections at ferrule connections, and corroded clamp contact surfaces all contribute to increases overall resistance of a jumper.*

| Figure 6-13 | Incorrect Jumper Positioning |

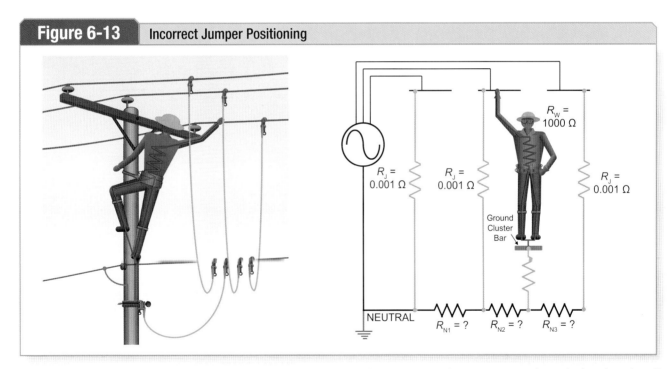

Figure 6-13. *During a fault current event, high amperage flowing from phase to phase must pass through short lengths off the neutral wire. The added resistances of an additional grounding jumper, two more contact surfaces, and a length of neutral conductor could increase the reaction time of over-current protection equipment. If the neutral conductor is of a reduced size or has less ampacity than the grounding jumpers, it could fuse between the grounding clamps, resulting in the loss of equipotential zone protection.*

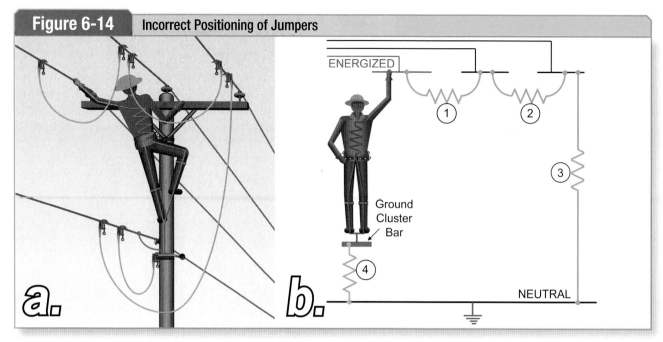

Figure 6-14. *(a) Incorrect positioning of jumpers could result in unacceptable voltage levels across the worker. (b) If the red phase were to become energized, this worker is in parallel with four grounding jumpers connected in series. The combined resistance of the four jumpers, associated connections, and short lengths of line conductor between the grounding clamps will increase the resistance between the energized red phase and the cluster bar. The total resistance of this grounding jumper arrangement will cause a greater voltage drop across, and thus increased body current flow through, the worker.*

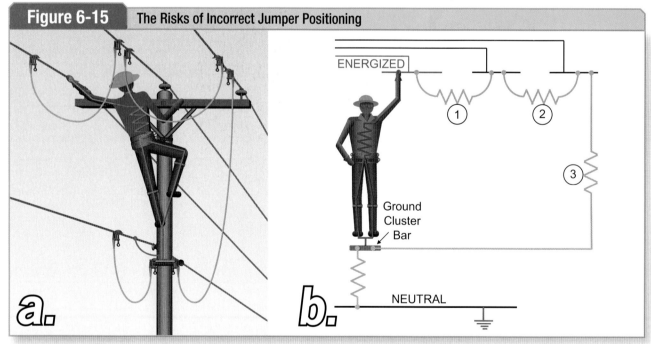

Figure 6-15. *(a) The grounding jumper connected from a phase wire directly to the cluster bar reduces the number of series linked jumpers to three. (b) If the worker is in contact with the energized red phase wire, he or she provides a parallel current branch and the series jumpers provide the other branch. The greater the resistance of the grounding jumper branch, the greater the body current through the worker. Although in an equipotential zone, the body current could exceed an acceptable level, putting the worker at risk.*

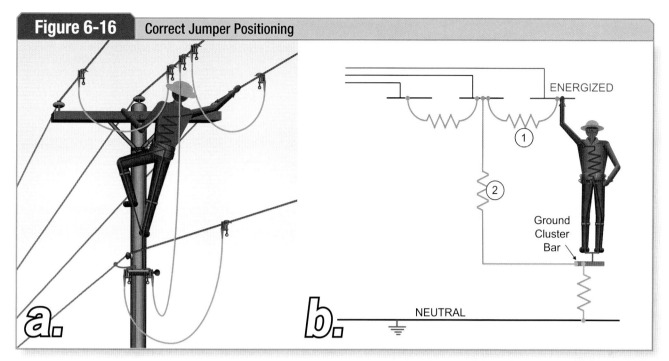

Figure 6-16   Correct Jumper Positioning

Figure 6-16. (a) On crossarm type construction, this grounding jumper arrangement provides the best worker protection. (b) A T configuration has a jumper from the middle phase wire to the cluster bar and provides the lowest resistance parallel branch to shunt fault current around the worker. If any of the lines become energized, there can be no more than two jumpers connected in a parallel branch between the worker's hand and the cluster bar. Remember, parallel circuit laws state that all branches have current flow and the branch with the lowest resistance will proportionally have the greatest current flow.

When incorrectly installed, the worker can have as many as four jumpers in parallel with the body.

Care should be taken to avoid incorrect jumper positioning. **See Figures 6-13, 6-14, and 6-15.**

CABLE REQUIREMENTS

Protective ground cables and accessories are also selected using ASTM tables. They have seven current-carrying ratings, the same as clamps. Cable must be copper, extra flexible, low in resistance, and jacketed to protect the strands. Aluminum cables are not used for protective grounds. Cable is selected to be the weakest link in the assembly.

Grounding cables are electrically tested on a regular schedule and after modification or sustaining a fault. An electrical acceptance test is performed on new grounding cables before use.

Protective grounding cables consist of appropriate lengths of suitable copper grounding cable, with electrically and mechanically compatible copper ferrules and clamps at each end. In addition, appropriate hot sticks are required for installing and removing the normally energized clamp end. Hot sticks are required for attaching ground end clamps if the grounded system and the worker are at different potentials. Cluster bars provide a low resistance means of connecting the ground end clamps.

The options vary widely when it comes to temporary grounding cable. Most grounding cables in use today are manufactured for another purpose—principally as welding cable. These highly flexible copper cables with jackets are manufactured according to appropriate ASTM standards and can be expected to perform satisfactorily as grounding cables.

Stranding for several classes of flexible cable in the sizes normally used for grounding cables is given in ASTM Standard F855.

Figure 6-17 | ASTM Standard F855

| Grade | Grounding Clamp Torque Strength, min | | | | Short Circuit Properties[A] | | | | | | | |
| | Yield[B] | | Ultimate | | Withstand Rating, Symmetrical kA RMS, 60 Hz | | | Ultimate Rating Capacity[CD] Symmetrical kA RMS, 60 Hz | | | | |
	lbf-in.	n-m	lbf-in.	n-m	15 cycles (250 ms)	30 cycles (500 ms)	Cooper cable size	15 cycles (250 ms)	30 cycles (500 ms)	60 cycles (1 s)	Maximum Copper Test Cable Size	Continuous Current Rating, A RMS, 60 Hz
1	280	32	330	37	14	10	#2	18	13	9	2/0	200
2	280	32	330	37	21	15	1/0	29	21	14	4/0	250
3	280	32	330	37	27	20	2/0	37	26	18	4/0	300
4	330	37	400	45	34	25	3/0	47	33	23	250 kcmil	350
5	330	37	400	45	43	30	4/0	59	42	29	250 kcmil	400
6	330	37	400	45	54	39	250 kcmil or 2 2/0	70	49	35	350 kcmil	450
7	330	37	400	45	74	54	350 kcmil or 2 4/0	98	69	48	550 kcmil	550

[A]Withstand and ultimate short circuit properties are based on performance with surges not exceeding 20% asymmetry factor (see 9.1 and 12.3.4.2)
[B]Yield shall mean no permanent deformation such that the clamp cannot be reused throughout its entire range of application.
[C]Ultimate rating represents a symmetrical current which the assembly or individual components shall carry for the specified time.
[D]Ultimate values are based upon application of Onderdonk's equation to 98% of nominal circular mil area allowed by Specifications B 172 and B 173.

Figure 6-17. The maximum fault current capability and continuous current rating varies depending on the type of AWG grounding cable used. rms = root mean square.

Table 1 of ASTM F855 Specifications for Temporary Protective Grounds to Be Used on De-energized Electric Power Lines and Equipment re-printed with permission from ASTM International. Copyright ASTM International, 100 Barr Harbor Drive, West Conshohocken, PA 19428. All Rights Reserved. Full standard available at www.astm.org.

Cable Size

The size of the grounding cable must be selected for the maximum anticipated (calculated) fault current at the worksite. The equipment shall have an ampacity greater than or equal to that of No. 2 AWG copper. In large substations, the maximum anticipated fault current may be high enough to require larger-diameter cables. If larger-diameter cables are not available, parallel cables (with the appropriate derating factor) may be used.

If the anticipated continuous current at the jobsite exceeds the continuous current rating for the grounding cable, a section of aluminum conductor or bus (including clamps) rated for the anticipated continuous current is used. Grounding cables are capable of handling the available continuous current. In areas where induced voltages may be a hazard, calculations are made to determine the magnitude and time characteristics of continuous current for grounding cables to be left in place for more than one day.

Cable sizes are in accordance with the maximum anticipated worksite fault current, the continuous (induced) current as the root mean square for the specific facility, or both. **See Figure 6-17.**

Protective grounds must be designed, assembled, and installed in a manner that satisfies the following basic criteria:

1. Protective grounding cables are capable of conducting the maximum anticipated fault current that could occur at the worksite if the deenergized, or electrically isolated, line or equipment becomes momentarily energized from any source. A grounding cable, which conducts the maximum anticipated fault

current, must also conduct the steady state current or currents induced by electromagnetic-coupled voltage on adjacent energized parallel lines.

2. The grounding cable must be rated to carry the maximum anticipated continuous current for the time that the grounding cable is in place.

3. The voltage drop across a protective grounding cable, when carrying maximum anticipated fault current, must be low enough to prevent hazardous current flow through the worker's body. The values of voltage drop must not exceed 75 volts for 30-hertz transmission line (500-millisecond) clearing.

4. The protective grounding cable must be terminated with clamps of adequate capacity and strength to withstand all electrical and mechanical forces present under maximum fault conditions.

5. The grounding cable must be easy and timely to apply, satisfy the requirements of field conditions, and adapt to a range of conductor, structural steel, and ground wire or rod sizes.

6. The cable length should be as short as practical for the specific task being performed.

The maximum anticipated fault current values given for protective ground cables, ferrules, and clamps are for 15- and 30-hertz clearing times. Continuous current–carrying capacities for copper cables are from 250 amperes for 1/0 AWG to 400 amperes for 4/0 AWG. Under continuous current conditions greater than the specified values, calculations indicate that the cable jacket begins to melt in approximately one minute and the copper begins to fuse in approximately three minutes.

Personnel working on grounded lines that cross fused lines, or some distribution voltage reclosers, should be aware of this hazard. If workers become aware of cable heating, they should move clear of situations that would place them in parallel with a deteriorated

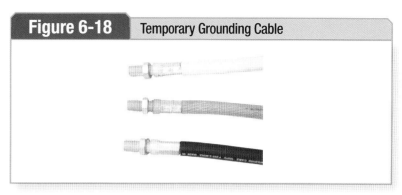

Figure 6-18. *Cable jacket coloring indicates the type of material used for the jacket.*

personal protective ground cable, warn their coworkers, and remain clear until the hazard has been removed. In this situation, the protective grounds are primarily for protection from induced voltage buildup at the worksite and not intended as back-up protection for accidental energization.

Cable Jackets

Cable jacket material is only rated at 600 volts. The jacket may be yellow, black, or clear. There are also jackets made with orange Type I elastomer welding cable. **See Figure 6-18.** Its primary purpose is to provide mechanical protection from damage to the extremely fine strands of copper wire. It cannot be considered insulation at distribution or transmission voltage levels.

There are two ASTM cable jacket types: elastomer and thermoplastic. **See Figure 6-19.** Type I elastomer cables are used in

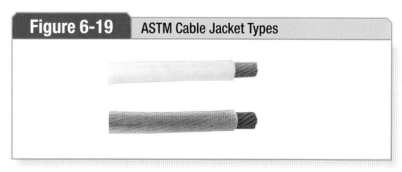

Figure 6-19. *Elastomer (top) and thermoplastic (bottom) cables are appropriate for different temperature ranges.*

temperatures as low as -40°F, whereas Type II cables can only be used down to -13°F. Both types can be used at temperatures as high as 194°F. Thermoplastic cables, also known as Type III cables, have a narrower temperature range, from 14°F to 140°F. They can only be used in well-ventilated areas; otherwise, they may create toxic gas when burning.

The flexible elastomer or thermoplastic jackets are manufactured, applied, and tested according to ASTM standards. Black and yellow jackets are usually neoprene rubber compounds, while clear jackets are ultraviolet inhibited polyvinyl chloride. All jackets should have the AWG size stamped or printed repeatedly along the length of the cable. The clear jacket allows easy visual inspection of the conductor for strand breakage, but becomes stiff and hard to handle at low temperatures and sometimes splits or shatters at very low temperatures.

Care should be used in handling and lifting grounding cables, because continuous flexing eventually breaks the conductor strands beneath the jacket. Sharp bends in the cable should be avoided.

EQUIPMENT GOVERNING STANDARDS

Reference to the available national standards can be used to assist in the equipment selection. ASTM F855 governs equipment standards. It has specifications for clamps, ferrules, cables, and full assemblies. However, the standard is for the manufacturer to develop and rate equipment and the employer or utility to select suitable equipment that meets its needs. It only specifies a maximum current and maximum time that the equipment will perform its task without failure. It does not address worker safety. **See Figure 6-20.**

The cable performance rating is based on melting calculations in the Onderdonk equation, which in turn is based on 1928 research by I.M. Onderdonk. Cable may separate in full melting time if hot and whipping. The Electrical Power Research Institute (Project No. RP2446) verified premature separation.

With ASTM F855, cable is selected as the weak link in the assembly. All other components must exceed the cable current versus time characteristics. **See Figure 6-21.**

As an example, assume the following:

$$I_F = 12,000 \text{ A}$$
$$t_{breaker} = 20 \text{ cycles (0.33 s)}$$
$$R = 0.09825 \text{ }\Omega\text{, or } 0.0009825 \text{ m}\Omega\text{, per } 1,000 \text{ ft}$$
$$V_{max} = 50 \text{ V}$$

The available 12,000 amperes for 20 cycles exceeds the AWG No. 2 rating for a 10-foot jumper assembly, so AWG 1/0 is selected. Resistance of 0.001 ohm per jumper assembly would then be as follows:

$$0.0009825 + 0.001 = 0.0009925$$

or approximately 1 mΩ.

If the worker can only contact one conductor, a 10-foot assembly consisting of AWG 1/0 would be suitable, providing a 30-volt drop across the worker. But often the worker may contact other phases than the one to which the jumper is attached.

Considering the positioning of the jumpers, up to four jumpers with two clamps each may be in parallel with the worker if care is not exercised in the placement. Assume the following:

$$J = \text{four 10-ft 1/0 AWG jumpers}$$
$$R_J = 1.98 \text{ m}\Omega$$
$$R_W = 1,000 \text{ }\Omega$$

The total jumper resistance is thus:

$$R_{J_T} = J \times R_J = 4 \times 1.98 = \text{approximately } 0.008 \text{ }\Omega\text{, or } 8 \text{ m}\Omega$$

Then the worker body voltage can be determined:

| Figure 6-20 | Conductor Withstand Rating vs AWG Size | | | |

ASTM Grade	Copper Cable Size	Withstand Current Non-fusing		Ultimate Current Fusing	
		(in thousands of amperes)			
		15 Cycles	30 Cycles	15 Cycles	30 Cycles
1	No. 2	14	10	18	13
2	1/0	21	15	29	21
3	2/0	27	20	37	26
4	3/0	34	25	47	33
5	4/0	43	30	59	42
6	250 kcmil or 2 2/0	54	39	70	49
7	350 kcmil or 2 4/0	74	54	98	69

Figure 6-20. The withstand rating of a conductor increases as the AWG size of the conductor increases. kcmil = thousand circular mils.

| Figure 6-21 | Conductor Resistances vs AWG Size | |

AWG Size	Resistance (in milliohms per foot)	ASTM Grade
No. 2	0.1563	1
1/0	0.09827	2
2/0	0.07793	3
3/0	0.06180	4
4/0	0.04901	5
250 kcmil	0.04231	6
350 kcmil	0.03022	7
No. 4	0.2485	
No. 6	0.3951	

Figure 6-21. The resistance of a conductor increases as the diameter of the conductor decreases. kcmil = thousand circular mils.

$$E_W = \frac{(R_{J_T})}{(R_W + R_{J_T})} \times I_F$$

$$= \frac{0.008}{(1,000 + 0.008)} \times 12,000 = 96 \text{ V}$$

This exceeds the allowed voltage of 50 volts. Another size must be chosen, such as 2/0 AWG with resistance of 1.78 milliohms per jumper:

$$R_{J_T} = J \times R_J = 4 \times 1.78$$
$$= 0.0071 \ \Omega, \text{ or } 7.1 \text{ m}\Omega$$

For 2/0 AWG, the worker body voltage is then as follows:

$$E_W = \frac{(R_{J_T})}{(R_W + R_{J_T})} \times I_F$$

$$= \frac{0.0071}{(1,000 + 0.0071)} \times 12,000 = 85 \text{ V}$$

This also exceeds the allowed 50 volts. Still another size must be chosen, such as 4/0 AWG, with four 10-foot jumpers at 1.5 milliohms each:

$$R_{J_T} = J \times R_J = 4 \times 1.5 = 0.006 \ \Omega, \text{ or } 6 \text{ m}\Omega$$

This results in the following:

$$E_W = \frac{(R_{J_T})}{(R_W + R_{J_T})} \times I_F$$
$$= \frac{0.006}{(1{,}000 + 0.006)} \times 12{,}000 = 72 \text{ V}$$

This still exceeds the allowed voltage. This means that another connection method should be chosen.

Careful correct positioning of the jumpers to the center phase of a 3-phase system limits the number of jumpers in parallel with the worker to two. **See Figure 6-22.**

Recalculating the parameters using 2/0 AWG but limited to two jumpers results in the following:

$$R_{J_T} = J \times R_J = 2 \times 1.78$$
$$= 0.00356 \ \Omega, \text{ or } 3.56 \text{ m}\Omega$$

Thus, the worker body voltage is as follows:

$$E_W = \frac{(R_{J_T})}{(R_W + R_{J_T})} \times I_F$$
$$= \frac{0.00356}{(1{,}000 + 0.00356)} \times 12{,}000 = 43 \text{ V}$$

This meets the requirements of both body current and voltage.

The designed jumper assembly is to be placed in parallel with the worker. Other jumpers that connect to a neutral or an earth connection need only to be sized to carry the current without fusing. Their voltage drop is not important for worker safety, because they are not in parallel with the worker.

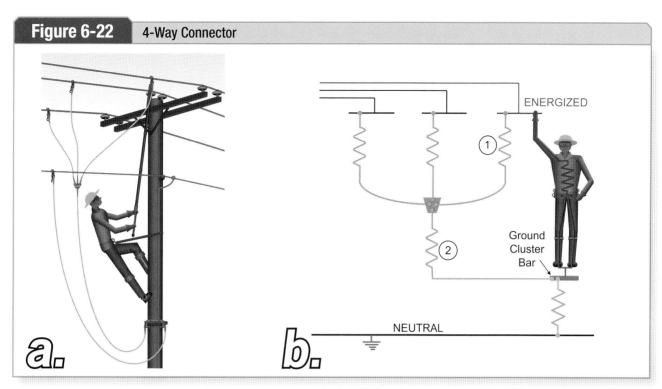

| Figure 6-22 | 4-Way Connector |

Figure 6-22. (a) The grounding set is fitted with a 4-way connector providing a common connection between the phase wire leads and the cluster bar. Use of this grounding set requires the worker to make fewer clamp to conductor connections. (b) During energization of one or all phase wires, the worker will always be two jumper leads from the body contact point to the cluster bar.

Summary

Accidentally reenergized "dead" lines do not cause most worker accidents, but they can occur. This makes it important to size and select grounding equipment so that it carries the maximum available fault current for the maximum time it may flow without fusing wherever a worker may be present. Equipment is also selected to meet the required worker body current and voltage specifications, and it is rated to meet the worksite requirements and worker's needs.

A personal protective ground assembly consists of a cable and two clamps. Such assemblies are placed so that they minimize the total resistance in parallel with a worker. Workers should know cable and clamp ratings, manufacturer's torque recommendations for eye screws and terminals, and the maximum applied hot stick that is normally acceptable. However, workers must remember that manufacturer's specifications are not reliable for worker safety. The specifications are the basis of the manufacturer's requirements only.

Review Questions

1. By design, the weakest part of a ground jumper assembly is the __?__ .
   a. cable
   b. clamp body
   c. ferrules
   d. movable clamp jaw

2. Flat faced ground clamps with T handles and set screws are ideal for connections to permanently grounded metal surfaces like beams. They are included in the ASTM Type __?__ category.
   a. I
   b. II
   c. III
   d. IV

3. Grounding clamps come in assorted body styles and are normally made of aluminum alloys or __?__ .
   a. brass
   b. bronze
   c. stainless steel
   d. titanium

4. A grounding jumper arrangement in a T configuration provides the best worker protection. If any phase wire of a three phase line becomes energized, there can be no more than __?__ jumpers connected in a parallel branch with the worker.
   a. 1
   b. 2
   c. 3
   d. 4

5. ASTM Type I and Type II cable jackets are rated at __?__ volts and provide protection for the fine copper conductor strands. It is not considered insulation at distribution or transmission levels.
   a. 240
   b. 480
   c. 600
   d. 750

Installation of Grounds

Electrical workers must have a basic understanding of electrical theory to facilitate the proper application of personal protective grounding equipment. Every conceivable work zone and scenario cannot be described. Workers must have a broad-based understanding that permits them to design a personal protective grounding work zone that ensures their personal protection. In the field, this involves the installation of the protective grounds. There is a logical pattern to follow when installing personal protective grounds. The line must be tested for voltage before attempting installation.

Objectives

» List the order of connection for the installation of personal protective grounds.

» Understand the factors that affect the installation and removal of personal protective grounds.

» Describe the factors that determine the maximum distance between jumper sets.

Chapter 7

Table of Contents

INSTALLATION OF GROUNDS SEQUENCE

Before work begins on a line, circuit, or piece of equipment that is to be deenergized—or more specifically, electrically isolated and grounded—clearance must be obtained. Clearance is a documented statement from the operations supervisor to an authorized individual declaring that the line or equipment to be worked on has been disconnected from all power sources and deenergized. The circuit may be energized from static or induced sources and is not considered "dead" until it has been grounded. Circuits in close proximity to heavily energized circuits (usually 500 kilovolts) may cause the personal protective ground cable to draw an unacceptable arc during application.

There is a logical pattern to follow when installing personal protective grounds:
1. Test the voltage to verify that the system has been deenergized.
2. Locate and clean clamps for jumping, as well as connections.

Reminder

Always check local safety rules for PPE when using sticks.

Figure 7-1 Testing the Line for Voltage

Figure 7-1. After isolation and before grounding jumpers are installed, OSHA law requires the line to be tested and found absent of nominal voltage.

3. Minimize the cable slack.
4. Fulfill the connection requirements.
5. Follow the assembly removal requirements.

Testing Voltage

The line, circuit, or piece of equipment must be tested for voltage before attempting installation. **See Figure 7-1.** Then by starting at the earth connection point, the voltage is maintained at 0 volts during the installation. It is at 0 volts because there is no current flow into the earth at this time, so no voltage is transferred to this connection point and the resistance of the earth does not come into the circuit.

The testing and order of installation and removal are specified by the U.S. Occupational Safety and Health Administration (OSHA). According to OSHA 29 CFR 1910, "Before any ground is installed, lines and equipment shall be tested and found absent of nominal voltage, unless a previously installed ground is present" (OSHA 29 CFR 1910.269(n)(5)) [8].

Voltage detection testing is the process of sensing voltage on a line—in other words, the process of determining whether line voltage is present. It is used to provide an indication of voltage levels and to ensure that the line has been deenergized or electrically isolated. Voltage detection should be used only as a secondary confirmation of electrical isolation and only after a clearance is in effect.

Several types of voltage detectors are commercially available. Three are in common use: the neon indicator, the hot-horn or noisy tester detector, and the multiple-range detector. Each voltage detector has its advantages and disadvantages. The worker should choose the detector most appropriate for the given circumstance.

The neon indicator is attached to the end of a live-line tool and positioned in the electrical field produced by the circuit. It produces a clear visual indication of an energized circuit. Neon indicators should be tested before and after each use. The neon voltage indicator provides a good visual indication; however, the detector is limited in application and may light up because of induced voltage from a nearby line.

The hot-horn or **noisy tester voltage detector** (NTVD), not to be confused with the noisy tester buzzing device, sounds an alarm to alert workers that voltage is present. The NTVD is often used to check areas above or below ground and areas around switchgear, substations, and overhead lines. Many NTVDs give a signal despite the type of voltage on the circuit. Other types of NTVDs are equipped with two pitches to differentiate between circuit- and electromagnetically induced voltages.

This detector is battery operated, with 4.5 or 9 volts depending upon the voltage detector, and is attached to the end of a live-line tool. NTVD operation may vary with the manufacturer; however, typically all that is involved is turning on the device and placing the detector in the field of the conductor. It is not necessary to put the device in contact with the circuit and in some cases can be dangerous to do so—the NTVD should not touch circuits containing 33 kilovolts or more. The manufacturer's specifications list the distances from the circuit that ensure safe and accurate results. **See Figure 7-2.**

Most NTVDs are supplied with test and disconnect switches. The instrument should be checked before and after each test to ensure proper and accurate usage.

There are several advantages to using an NTVD. First, the worker can receive an approximation of the voltage without making contact with the circuit. In addition, the NTVD is relatively light and

Figure 7-2	NTVD Operating Characteristics	
Distance from Conductor		**Kilovolts on Conductor**
25 mm	(1 in)	4
102 mm	(4 in)	13
305 mm	(1 ft)	26
457 mm	(1 ft 6 in)	33
0.9 m	(3 ft)	110
1.8 m	(6 ft)	230

Figure 7-2. Operating characteristics for the NTVD vary depending on the manufacturer but fall within a general range.

inexpensive and is one of the simplest voltage detectors to use. The disadvantages are that the device is limited to a maximum of about 250 kilovolts and that it does not specifically indicate estimated voltage.

The multiple-range voltage detector (MRVD) is essentially a multiple-range field-intensity meter equipped with an internally connected steel contact hook mounted on a live-line tool. To operate the MRVD, a selector switch is activated, which enables the worker to vary the kilovolt ranges. The worker can then use the MRVD to approximate phase-to-phase voltages by hanging the steel contact hook on the circuit. The MRVD uses field intensity to estimate phase-to-phase voltage, rather than the actual voltage and difference in potential. Therefore, the MRVD is an inaccurate instrument, and all readings should be regarded as estimates. If the interpretation of the meter reading is questioned, the worker should assume that the line is energized and use other methods to determine the electrical status of the circuit.

The MRVD is battery operated and equipped with an internal battery circuit and a test button. The MRVD should be checked before and after each test.

There are many advantages to using an MRVD:
- The MRVD provides a more reliable indication than other voltage detectors of the voltage differences between energized circuits and circuits that have been deenergized, or electrically isolated, from all sources of primary system energy.
- The device provides the worker with a specific approximation of the voltage on line.
- On certain MRVDs, the operating voltages may be as high as 550 kilovolts.

However, the MRVD has some important disadvantages:
- To operate the MRVD, the device must come in contact with the circuit.
- The device is heavier and more expensive than other voltage detectors.
- If the MRVD is close to a ground or to another energized circuit, the reading registers higher than the actual voltage on the measured circuit. The opposite is true if the MRVD is near a circuit operating at the same voltage.

Cleaning Connections

The surface of the structure ground wire, ground rod, or metal structure member to which the ground-end clamp is to be applied is usually corroded, contaminated, or insulated by paint. High levels of corrosion or a paint coating on a tower present a high resistance to the flow of current. The heat generated in any high-resistance connection may burn the paint away or melt the metal at the point of contact, resulting in a loss of clamp torque and a high-current arc. The clamp may then come off its connection, losing the protection for the worker.

Each connection should be cleaned before a clamp is applied. At a minimum, clamps with serrated jaws can be used. **See Figure 7-3.**

Wire brushes on hot sticks can be used to clean conductor surfaces before the grounding clamps are installed. **See Figure 7-4.** The conductor must be cleaned with a wire brush attached to a

| **Figure 7-3** | **Conductor Cleaning Clamps** |

Figure 7-3. The serrated jaws on a type C clamp can remove oxidation from conductors when rocked fore and aft before tightening.

| Figure 7-4 | Wire Brushes |

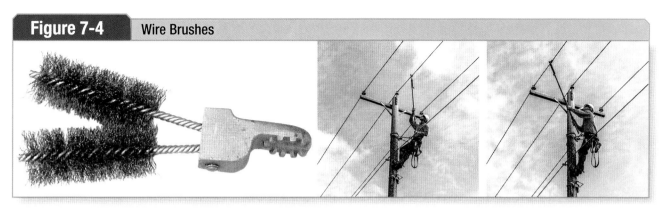

Figure 7-4. *Wire brushes on hot sticks can be used to clean conductors.*

hot stick, because the conductor is considered energized until it is properly grounded. The cleaning effect of wire brushing is nearly gone within 20 minutes, requiring the clamp to be applied immediately after brushing.

Tower steel can be sanded, scraped, or wire brushed. However, the highly resistive protective oxide on weathered or painted steel should not be removed. Scraping the paint and refinishing seldom provide an adequate electrical connection. The aluminum pipe bus or conductor to which the conductor clamp is to be applied also has a high-resistance oxide film. Grounding is best accomplished by welding a copper bar, steel bar, or stainless steel nut, to which a threaded copper stud can be inserted, at each grounding location. Grounds may be extended to a ground rod or to the overhead ground wire.

Weathering steel poles should be constructed with bonds between crossarms and poles and between slip joints to ensure electrical continuity. An example of slip-joint structure is a light-duty steel pole. These galvanized poles have a nonconductive wrap in the corrosion active zone that extends approximately 0.61 meter (2 feet) above and below ground. Vehicles and equipment are grounded to the grounding lug, which is provided above the protective wrap.

A bond is the electrical interconnection of conductive parts to maintain a common electrical voltage [1]. Slip-joint structures should have bonding cables permanently attached to each slip joint, or joint resistance should be measured on selected structures after installation and period-

ically as maintenance personnel deem necessary. Surfaces where protective grounds are to be attached are cleaned before cable attachment to ensure a proper electrical contact. If bonding straps are not part of the structure, ground cables must be extended to a ground rod or to the overhead ground wire.

Minimizing Cable Slack

Clamps must be positioned to minimize the slack in the cables. The worker should never place more than one conductor into the jaws of a single clamp.

Slack in the installed cables should be minimal to reduce possible injury to workers due to the whipping action from fault currents. Resistance in the cable increases with cable length, and excessive length exceeds the tolerable voltage drop. Excessive cable lengths should be avoided by selecting grounding cables of the approximate required length. Cables that are longer than necessary also tend to twist or coil, which reduces the current-carrying capacity of the cable. Excess cable should never be wrapped around a metal structure or coiled. A wrapped or coiled cable creates a transformer effect, which again reduces the current-carrying capacity of the cable and, if the fault or induced current is high enough, destroys the cable.

Connection Requirements

Before installation, each grounding cable assembly is visually inspected for mechanical damage. Suspect cables shall be removed from service. Grounds should be placed as near the worksite as practical. If installing a grounding cable is impractical or if it would create an unsafe condition, the ground cable should not be installed and the circuit should be worked as if it were energized at system voltage. Hot sticks are used to physically check ground clamps for tightness. When ground resistance is suspect, such as in rocky soil or if buried pole-to-pole ground wire ties for a wood pole structure are deteriorated, the overhead ground wire may be used to provide a better ground than provided by butt-wrapped poles, steel structure foundations, or ground rods. Seventy to ninety percent of fault current flows to the overhead ground wire, which makes this wire a good choice for grounding. Buried pole-to-pole ground wire ties are not to be relied upon for maintenance grounding activities.

Two key grounding rules must be followed: (1) Do not clamp more than one conductor per clamp, and (2) derate jumpers if multiple ones are required to carry the high fault current. It is also important to maintain safe worker distance until the line is properly grounded. **See Figure 7-5.**

> **Reminder**
>
> If there is no pole ground present, an additional ground jumper must be attached from the cluster bar to a driven ground rod.

OSHA 29 CFR 1910.269(n)(6) states, "When a ground is to be attached to a line or to equipment, the ground-end connection shall be attached first, and then the other end shall be attached by means of a live-line tool". The first system connection should be to the closest neutral or conductor. Then each of the other conductors is grounded, working toward the top of a distribution structure. The following order of connection should be followed:

1. Connection to tower, or earth
2. Connection to neutral
3. Neutral to nearest-phase conductor
4. Nearest-phase conductor to next-closest-phase conductor
5. Next-closest-phase conductor to furthest conductor
6. Connection of one of the preceding to the static wire, if present

The ground-end clamp of each grounding cable is always the first connection made and the last to be removed. Ground-end clamps are attached by hot stick if the grounded system and the worker are at different potentials. Line and substation personnel often use circuit-end clamps with eye screws for installation by means of "grip all" or "shotgun" hot sticks. Hot sticks used for grounding should be given the same care, inspection, and testing as those used for live work. **See Figure 7-6.**

The circuit-end clamps of grounding cables are always connected and disconnected by using hot sticks of a length and rating for the system voltage of the circuit or equipment. Workers must stay clear of the grounding cable while applying the grounding cable to the circuit or equipment. The practice of holding the cable near the base of the hot stick to lighten the load on the head of the stick is strictly prohibited. A coworker should assist in applying heavy grounds by holding the ground cable with another hot stick or by using a "shepherd hook" with a pulley and nonconductive rope to hoist the grounding cable into position. After the ground-end connection has been secured, the circuit-end clamp should be connected in turn to the nearest

| Figure 7-5 | Maintain Minimum Approach Distance |

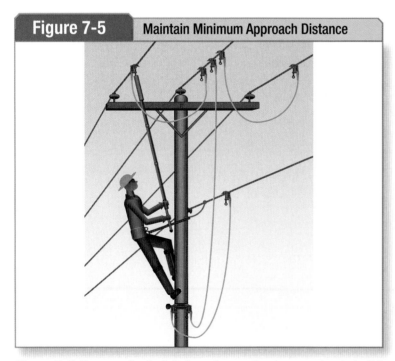

Figure 7-5. Because the installation of grounding jumpers is a hot stick procedure, violation of the minimum approach distance must be avoided until after all the conductors are properly grounded.

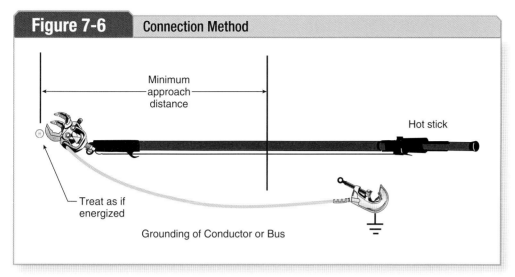

Figure 7-6 | Connection Method

Minimum approach distance

Hot stick

Treat as if energized

Grounding of Conductor or Bus

Figure 7-6. A safe distance must be maintained when grounding a conductor or bus.

circuit, proceeding outward and upward until all necessary phases have been grounded.

If the available fault current exceeds the current capability of the assembly, a larger ground cable or additional assemblies of the same size and approximate length may be placed in parallel. The cables are placed as close together as possible to minimize coupling. **See Figure 7-7.**

Cable lengths should not be extended by hooking cable clamps together or attaching them to an intermediate conductor except as permitted when grounding cluster bars. Commercial cable couplers that are rated for maximum anticipated fault current are available. Cable couplers are convenient for keeping substation and vehicle grounding cables reasonably short.

The division of current between parallel grounds depends upon the total resistance of each grounding cable, including the connection resistance. If the fault current to be carried by the cables would be near their combined capacity, it would be possible for the cable with the lower resistance to be overloaded. This could cause it to fail, which would allow the total fault current to appear on the other cable, causing it to fail as well. It is not normally practical to ensure that parallel cables are identical. Each of the assemblies should

have its rating reduced by 10% to allow for variations in connection placement and unequal resistances. For simplicity, a derating multiplier of 0.9 can be used for each cable. For example, for a root-mean-square

Figure 7-7 | Paralleled Jumpers

Figure 7-7. In situations where the available fault current is greater than the rated capacity of the grounding jumpers on hand, paralleling jumpers is an acceptable solution. Cables of the same size and approximately the same length are required. Position paralleled jumpers as close together as possible. When paralleled, the rating must be reduced by 10% if the cables are restrained or by 20% if unrestrained.

fault current capability of 20,000 amperes, two 2/0 American Wire Gauge (AWG) copper cables in parallel can carry $2 \times (20,000 \times 0.9) = 36,000$ amperes for 30 cycles (500 milliseconds).

Multiple cables should be bound or twisted together. The cables are tied or twisted together to maximize the current-carrying capacity of the cable set; otherwise, the reduction factor is set as 0.8 to compensate for the mechanical and induced forces on unbound or non-twisted cables. For example, the fault 20,000-amperes current capability, two nontwisted 2/0 AWG copper cables would then can carry $2 \times (20,000 \times 0.8) = 32,000$ amperes for 30 cycles.

When subconductor hardware is separated or when subconductor bonding is suspect, the subconductors (on the phase being worked) are bonded by a cable of the same size as the protective grounds in use. Insulated phase spacers could cause the worker to experience unbalanced subconductor currents; therefore, the subconductors should be bonded during insulated spacer work.

The worksite must not be considered safely grounded until all jumpers have been installed in case a fault should occur during the installation.

Doubling grounds at the worksite, or using other equipment found to be suitable, can be a method of reducing the required size of the equipment. If one set is placed on either side of the worksite, similar to paralleling at a single site, the current division allows lower-rated (smaller) equipment to be used at the worksite.

The use of multiple remote grounds to reduce the current at the worksite does not remove the necessity of providing the protection at the worksite. Until all grounds are installed, the site must be considered energized and all work must be done using hot sticks.

Multiple crews may work on radial lines provided that each crew uses its own worksite grounding and its own clearance. Each crew is responsible for receiving clearance and following grounding work procedure. Multiple crews should not work on a line paralleling an energized line or lines unless it has been determined that the magnitude of the circulating ground currents is at an acceptable level.

Assembly Removal Requirements

Removal of the protective grounding cable assemblies is the reverse of the installation, with the conductor or equipment end removed by hot stick first and the grounded end removed last. As stated in OSHA 29 CFR 1910.269(n)(7), "When a ground is to be removed, the grounding device shall be removed from the line or equipment using a live-line tool before the ground-end connection is removed".

INSTALLATION EXAMPLES

Ground installation involves connecting all phase conductors together. There are typically three conductors: nearest, next closest, and farthest from the neutral. With 3-phase grounding, protective grounding cables are installed so that all phases of lines, buses, equipment, and apparatus are visibly and effectively bonded together in a multiphase "short" and connected to ground at the worksite. Conductive objects within reach of any worker should be bonded to this grounding system. Equipment may be temporarily unbonded from the system to perform necessary maintenance functions such as power factor tests. Care must be taken on double-circuit structures to ensure that live work procedures and approach distances are enforced for the energized circuit.

Single- or 2-phase grounding is normally used only in adverse weather conditions or when 3-phase grounding creates a greater hazard (such as climbing a double-circuit structure to ground the upper phases when only the lower phase is to be worked). Single-phase grounding is not allowed in substations.

With single-phase grounding, the ungrounded phases are treated as if energized at system voltage, and the appropriate live work minimum approach distances apply. Ungrounded phases exposed to induced currents are at less than system operating voltage; however, using a lower minimum approach distance than required by system operating voltage is prohibited.

The probability of a fault occurring during the single-phase grounding work process is small compared to unavoidable physical and weather hazards; however, workers must be aware that combining grounded and live work procedures requires additional awareness. If a supervisor determines that single-phase grounding is the safest for all concerned, the procedure should be discussed with the crew, and the entire crew should be in agreement with the work procedure.

Staged fault tests by the Western Area Power Administration have indicated that there is no significant difference between 3-phase and single-phase fault current distribution at the worksite on steel structures; however, the staged fault tests indicate that there can be a significant fault current distribution difference on multipole wood structures. Eighty to 90% of a fault current exits the worksite through the overhead ground wires (where they exist). Although fault current is evenly distributed among overhead ground wires on steel structures, the fault current distribution on wood structures depends on the electrical potential difference between poles. Deterioration of butt wrap, underground pole-to-pole ties, structure ground wires, and connections between structure ground wire and hardware requires that each structure be treated uniquely for the work practice being employed.

Worksite Equipotential or Single-Point Grounding

To ensure the fast trip-out operation of circuit protection devices, the installation of a complete grounding set bonding the phases, the neutral and earth together is essential. In a case of re-energization of all phases, the cross-phase grounding jumpers will cause a phase-to-phase fault alerting and operating overcurrent protection equipment. If only one phase is energized, the grounding jumper connecting the phases to neutral and earth will create a ground fault that will initiate the operation of the protective switchgear. Only by properly adding a cluster

bracket with a personal grounding jumper to the trip-grounding set can an equipotential zone be created to guarantee an aloft worker's safety. The full grounding set with the personal low resistance jumper and cluster bar are most often installed at the worksite. This method is referred to as Single-Point Grounding. **See Figure 7-8.**

Worksite Located at a Limited Distance from a Full Grounding Set

There are situations where having the phase-to-phase and phase-to-ground jumpers installed on an adjacent pole would be advantageous. When work is to be done on a structure one span away from where protective grounds are installed, a worker can be protected within an equipotential zone by the installation of a cluster bar and a grounding jumper or jumpers. **See Figure** 7-9.

| Figure 7-8 | Equipotential Grounding |

Figure 7-8. All three phases are cross-connected and a jumper from center phase is dropped to the cluster bar. (a) Because this circuit has an available neutral, which is the best ground electrode, it is connected to the cluster bar with a jumper. (b) This three wire delta line is without a neutral, so a long ground cable must be used to connect the cluster bar to the temporary ground rod.

At the location where protective grounds are installed, the phases and neutral are joined together and in case of induction or accidental re-energization, the potential across these lines will be zero. A potential difference across the lines and neutral will exist at distances away from the grounds. As the distance from the grounding set is increased, the potential difference across the phase wires and neutral also increases.

A worker within 300 feet of a complete grounding set must install a cluster bar with a personal jumper connected to any one of the conductors on the structure. He may contact any conductor on the pole and benefit from equipotential zone protection.

When the distance from the ground set is more than 300 feet, the potential between the phases and neutral can be reach hazardous levels. To protect workers at this increased distance, the cluster bar is connected with a jumper to the neutral. Another grounding jumper is connected from the cluster bar to the phase conductor being contacted. If the worker must contact more than one phase conductor on the structure, the grounding jumper is transferred to the phase wire being worked. Connecting the grounding jumpers from the cluster bar to the neutral and from the cluster bar to the phase being worked ensures that a low resistance jumper is in parallel with the worker. With the additional cluster bar to phase grounding jumper, this grounding method can be used at worksites more than one span away from the complete grounding set.

Equipotential Protection Between Grounds Installed on Remote Structures

There are circumstances where it may not be practical to install complete grounding sets at the work site. An example of an alternate system could be placement of a full 3-phase grounding set on either side of the worksite, similar to bracket grounding. However, in this case, a worker also uses a personal ground composed of a cluster bar, a jumper from the cluster bar to neutral, and a jumper from the cluster bar to the phase that is to be contacted. This personal ground moves from worksite to worksite as the worker relocates. The personal ground uses fewer components and is removed, relocated, and reinstalled as the worksite moves between the bracket grounds. System protection is provided by adjacent jumpers. They are sufficient to alert the circuit protection devices of the presence of a fault. The personal jumper (cluster bar plus line and neutral jumpers) provides worker protection.

Some variables must be evaluated to determine the minimum distance from the worksite. Bracket grounding away from the worksite requires a neutral. In addition, the allowed distance to remote grounds depends on the following variables:

- Fault current available
- Size (resistance) of conductors
- Size (resistance) of neutral
- Use of personal ground

The personal ground only provides an equipotential zone for contacting the grounded phase. No protection is provided if contact is made to other conductors, guy cables, or other system components near the restricted worksite but outside of the equipotential zone.

An alternative to this bracket grounding variation requires trip grounds installed one span away. Single point grounds installed at the adjacent structure provide phase-to-phase and phase-to-ground fault current paths in the event of accidental energization. The worker is within an equipotential zone when the personal jumper is connected to any grounded conductor on the structure. If the neutral is of a reduced size, as is often the case on distribution circuits, it would be advisable to connect the personal jumper to one of the phase wires of lower resistance.

A grounding jumper from the cluster bar to the phase being worked can be added. This additional jumper method is required if the distance from the adjacent pole complete grounding set is 300 feet or more. The distance between the poles

Figure 7-9 | Grounding Set Installed One Span from Worker

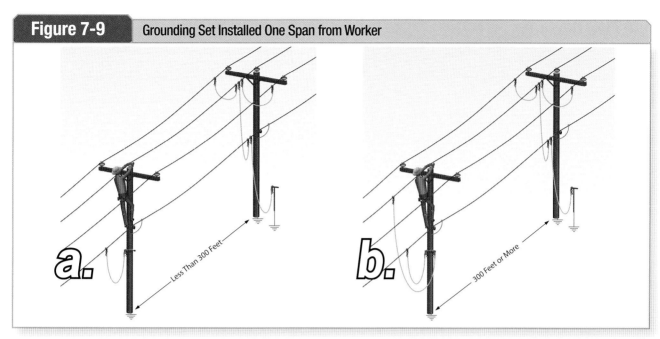

Figure 7-9. *Phase-to-phase, phase-to-neutral, and neutral-to-earth grounding jumpers can be installed at a distance from the worksite. If the line becomes energized, these grounds will alert and trip the over-current protection equipment. (a) A worker at less than 300 feet away from the installed grounds is positioned above a cluster bar and a personal protective jumper is connected to the system neutral. (b) If the worksite is at a distance of 300 feet or more from the installed grounding set, an additional grounding jumper is attached from the cluster bar to the conductor being worked. The key to worker protection in these examples is the equipotential zone created by installation of the cluster bar and personal grounding jumper.*

must be known or measured. This two jumper method provides a greater level of protection for the worker at distances more or less than 300 feet.

In most cases, a complete set of grounds installed within 300 feet of the pole being worked is considered to be grounding at the point of work. Utility and employer working rules vary and must be known before selecting grounding locations.

While these methods provide the required protection in a limited or reduced manner and increase productivity in some cases, they may not be appropriate for all situations. The complete personal protective grounding method must be used wherever possible to maximize worker protection.

Single Point Master Ground Set Location

Analytical circuit studies have been done proving that workers are provided greater protection when a complete set of grounding cables are installed between the worker and the energized source. These studies have found that at very high fault current levels, a grounding set installed at a location that places the worker between the grounds and the source can result in fatal worker body currents. Placement of the ground cables on the source side, as opposed to the load side of the worker, at a distance of as little as three feet can make the difference between acceptable and unacceptable body current levels.

Most isolated sections of distribution and transmission lines can become energized from either side of the work site due to contact with another energized circuit, voltage backfeed from a customer's cogeneration installation, lightning strikes, or an improper switching procedure. Because these examples and others make it difficult to predict the direction from which a line may become energized, workers must

Figure 7-10 | Vertical Construction

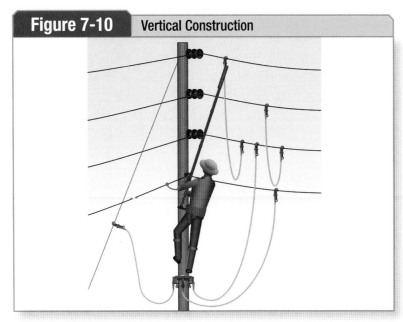

Figure 7-10. When installing ground cables on vertical tangents, dead ends, or running angles, it is best to work from the lowest conductor up. A T configuration provides the best protection and ensures that the worker cannot be in contact with a conductor more than two jumpers from the cluster bracket.

Figure 7-11 | Cable Clamp Attachment

Figure 7-11. In this crossarm application, the grounding set is in balance when installed in a T-configuration. A worker should take advantage for the entire length of the grip-all stick and maintain a generous approach distance to the phase conductors. The clamps are secured to the line conductors and never over the armor rod.

protect themselves from energization from either side of the work site. This is especially true when work is performed on large conductors or under any condition that can cause high fault current levels. Because single point grounding has limitations due to available high fault currents and specific job locations, it is not always a viable grounding method. A variation of the bracket method placing the worker and a personal jumper with cluster bar in an envelope between two complete grounding sets is the preferred method in these situations.

Structure Setups

Vertical running corner, vertical running deadend, and crossarm setups are used. For all three setups, a jumper connects the cluster bar to neutral. Another jumper connects the neutral to the closest phase. Jumpers thus connect all three phases.

Vertical Running Corner. For a vertical running corner, the cluster bar is mounted below the work area. **See Figure 7-10.**

Cluster bars should be mounted below the worker's feet and as near to conductor level as possible. Cluster bars must have an attached bonding lead and should be bonded to the pole ground wire at the mounting location. They may be connected to the cluster bar, to ground, and to neutral. Structure pole ground wires used in the grounding system are inspected before attaching the cluster bar ground lead to determine that these wires have not been deteriorated, cut, damaged, or removed. Personal protective grounding cables are connected between the grounding cluster bars and the phase conductors to provide a solid ground. Structures without pole ground wires or those whose structure ground wires are damaged or of questionable condition have the grounding cluster bars connected to temporary ground rods.

Vertical Deadend. When applying personal protective ground cables to wood pole structures, workers may use a grounding cluster bar to connect each conductor grounding cable to a pole ground wire. The cluster bar for a vertical deadend is mounted below the work area.

Crossarm Application. Grounding sets are available in 3-phase, 4-cable configurations or as individual single-cable sets. **See Figure 7-11.**

Crossarms are often found on composite structures constructed of two or more different materials (such as wood poles with steel or fiberglass crossarms). Concrete and composite structures usually have a structure ground wire attached to the surface much the same as wood poles. Metal crossarms should be bonded to the structure ground wire during installation. If a structure ground wire is not available, ground cables must be extended to a ground rod or to the overhead ground wire.

Wood Pole Structures

There are several 3-phase grounding applications for wood pole structures. The center phase conductor is connected to the grounding system of each pole. **See Figure 7-12.**

Grounding can also be done with double cluster bars and overhead ground wires. **See Figure 7-13.**

There are two important things to note when considering this type of grounding:

1. Workers should add a ground rod and cable to an ungrounded structure or to structure grounds that are suspect. The ground rod cable is attached to the cluster bar first with subsequent cables continuing from the cluster bar.

2. Personal ground cables connected to overhead ground wires may be attached either to the cluster bar or to a grounded phase conductor. In either of these cases, the structure ground is connected to the cluster bar and a solid electrical bond exists between the overhead ground wire and the rest of the system.

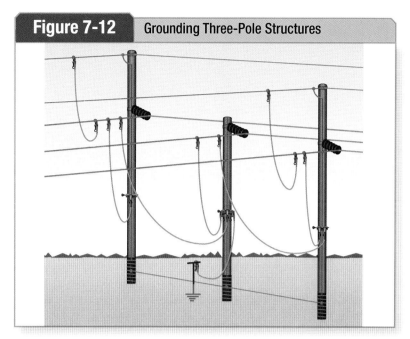

| Figure 7-12 | Grounding Three-Pole Structures |

Figure 7-12. Equipotential zones are formed above the cluster bars on each of the three poles. Two grounding jumpers connected at cluster bars provide cross-phase connections. A similar grounding cable and bracket arrangement can be applied to a three-pole double dead-end structure.

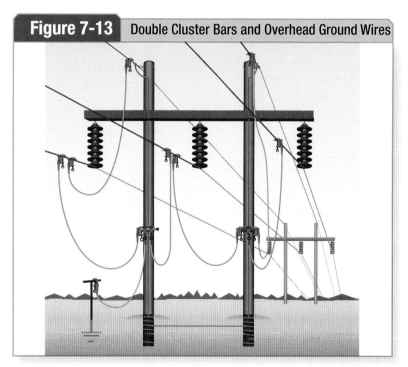

| Figure 7-13 | Double Cluster Bars and Overhead Ground Wires |

Figure 7-13. An equipotential zone provides worker protection on both poles by using a cluster bar on each pole.

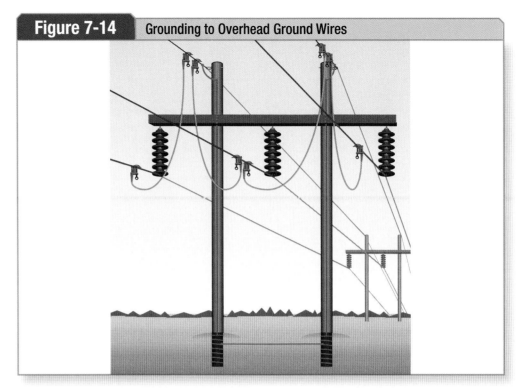

Figure 7-14. *Grounding jumpers connected to the overhead ground wires are necessary when removing hardware.*

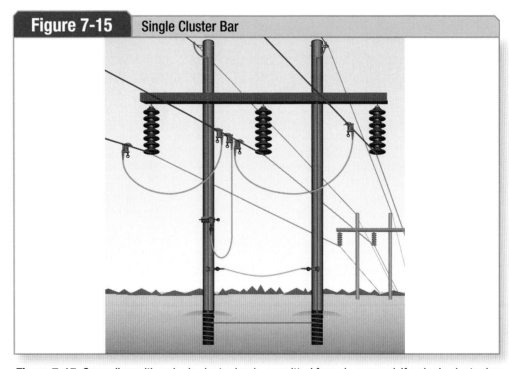

Figure 7-15. *Grounding with a single cluster bar is permitted for pole removal. If a single cluster bar is used, workers should stay 10 feet away from the ungrounded pole unless the poles are bonded together. When a pole is to be replaced, the tie may be removed once the pole-ground has been electrically isolated from the grounding system.*

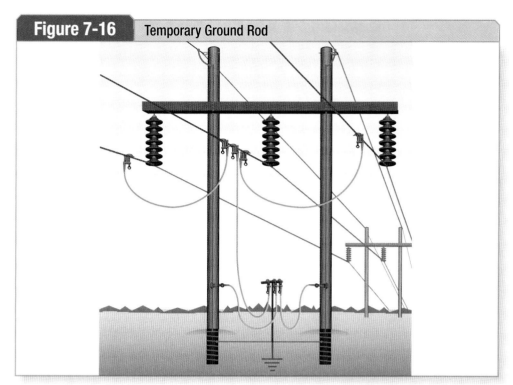

Figure 7-16. Temporary Ground Rod

Figure 7-16. When grounding with a temporary ground rod, the pole ground must be attached before the conductors. A temporary ground rod may be used in lieu of cluster bars provided that the pole grounds are attached to the ground rod prior to attaching to the conductors.

When hardware is to be disconnected or removed, a ground cable must be placed between the overhead ground wire and the structure ground to maintain grounding system continuity. **See Figure 7-14.**

Cluster bars are not required on both poles in situations such as pole change out. The pole grounds must be bonded at the base by a protective ground to keep each pole at the same potential until the pole being removed is isolated from the rest of the structure. The ground may then be removed with a hot stick. Protective grounds on the new pole are installed in reverse order.

If a single cluster bar is to be used, workers should stay 10 feet from the ungrounded pole unless the poles are bonded together. **See Figure 7-15.** When a pole is being replaced, the tie may be removed once the pole ground has been electrically isolated from the grounding system.

If there is no pole ground wire, the cluster bar for each pole is connected to a common driven ground rod with a grounding cable or cables. This temporary ground rod may be used in lieu of cluster bars provided that the pole grounds are attached to the ground rod before attaching the conductors. **See Figure 7-16.**

For the best effect, ground rods should be installed to full depth. Multirod separation equal to twice the depth should be maintained.

Temporary ground rods are available in a driven form or with a T-handle and screw-in auger tip. They must meet one of the following specifications:

1. A bronze, copper, or copper-weld rod with a minimum diameter of 16 millimeters (5/8 inch) and length of at least 1.8 meters (6 feet), driven to a depth of at least 1.5 meters (5 feet)

2. A 1.8-meter (6-foot), screw-type ground rod, consisting of a copper-weld shaft with a minimum diameter of 16 millimeters (5/8 inch) and a bronze auger bit and bronze T-handle, screwed to a depth of at least 1.5

Figure 7-17. *Four-wire wye lines have neutral conductors with many ground points. During a fault current event, the neutral provides a continuous low-resistance path back to the source substation ground mat. On wye circuits, the system neutral is the most effective ground electrode. Because all the pole grounds on a wye line are connected to the neutral, the earth and neutral provide parallel return current paths. Some employers may also require the addition of a temporary ground rod and grounding cable.*

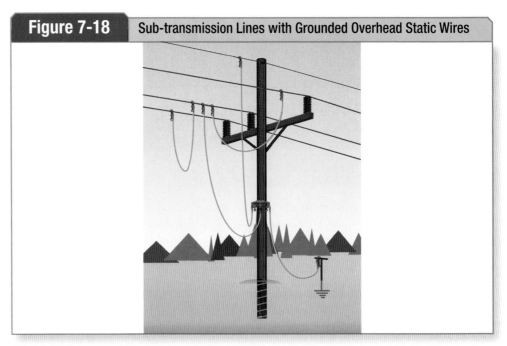

Figure 7-18. *Overhead static or shield wires are designed for lightning protection and are usually galvanized steel conductors. The pole ground wires are attached with bolted steel connectors. When the static or shield wire is within the work area, it must be electrically connected to extend the equipotential work zone. Because the static wire is a higher-resistance fault current return path, in some cases it may be necessary to install a temporary ground rod to lower the resistance of the earth return path.*

meters (5 feet), with the T-handle tightly connected to the rod

Because screw-type ground rods disturb the entire earth contact area, they may not be as efficient as driven ground rods.

The 1.5-meter (5-foot) depth is preferred. If a temporary rod cannot be driven or screwed to this depth, one or more additional rods should be driven or screwed so that a total of at least 1.5 meters (5 feet) of rod is buried. These rods are bonded together with grounding cables before installing phase grounds. The rods should be placed 1.5 to 3 meters (5 to 10 feet) apart; however, a 3-meter (10-foot) approach distance from all ground rods should be maintained. Overhead ground wires may be used to bond the conductors provided that these wires are electrically bonded to the structure ground, either permanently or by personal protective grounds.

Fault tests were conducted by the Western Area Power Administration on wood H-frames with a deteriorated pole-to-pole tie. **See Figure 7-17.**

Because the static wire is a higher resistance fault current return path, in some cases it may be necessary to install a temporary ground rod to lower the resistance of the earth return path. **See Figure 7-18.**

The tests indicated that the touch voltage, near the grounded pole, increases by approximately 50% with single-phase grounding. Therefore, single-phase grounding on wood H-frames should only be used when 3-phase grounding is not practical, and it should only be allowed if both pole grounds are bonded together with a grounding cable. **See Figure 7-19.**

Underground pole-to-pole ties must not be relied upon for completion of the grounding system. The underground pole-to-pole tie should be considered nonexistent. The structure ground wires on both poles should be bonded together to ensure distribution of the fault current to both overhead ground wires. **See Figure 7-20.**

Lattice Tower

A steel tower, or lattice tower, used for transmission is connected to earth by

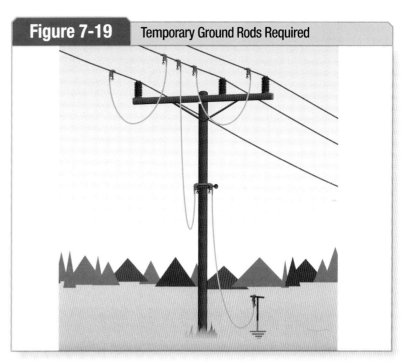

Figure 7-19 Temporary Ground Rods Required

Figure 7-19. A sub-transmission line may be constructed without a neutral or overhead grounded static wire. When grounding three wire lines of this type, a temporary ground rod must be installed and connected to the system.

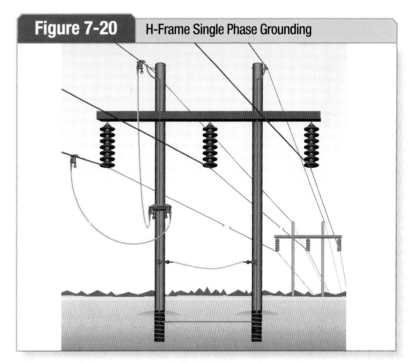

Figure 7-20 H-Frame Single Phase Grounding

Figure 7-20. A potential difference between the two poles can exist due to deterioration of underground pole-to-pole ties, butt wraps, pole ground wires, and bolted hardware connections. To ensure fault current is evenly distributed between the overhead ground wires, a grounding jumper is used to bond the two pole ground wires together.

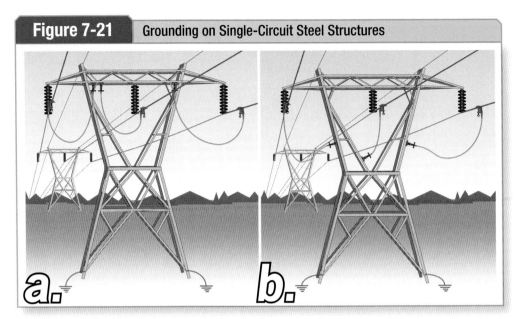

| Figure 7-21 | Grounding on Single-Circuit Steel Structures |

Figure 7-21. Grounding jumpers used on lattice steel structures are fitted with Type III, T-handle flat face ground clamps for connections to the angle iron. (a) On structures with ample conductor to tower distance, the preferred installation method is to attach the ground end of the jumper to the bridge above. (b) On lower-voltage lines, ground clamps can be attached to the tower from a position below the conductors. This alternative approach may be more practical; however, it is not the preferred method.

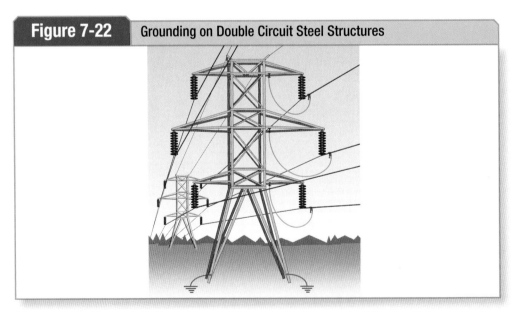

| Figure 7-22 | Grounding on Double Circuit Steel Structures |

Figure 7-22. The installation of ground to one circuit on a double circuit tower is done beginning with the lowest conductor. The middle conductor is grounded next, followed by the top conductor. The removal of the grounding jumpers is done from the top down. As always, the flat jaw clamp is connected to the grounded tower body before the line end of the jumper is attached to the conductor with a hot stick. When removing a grounding cable, the line end must be disconnected before the grounded tower end is detached.

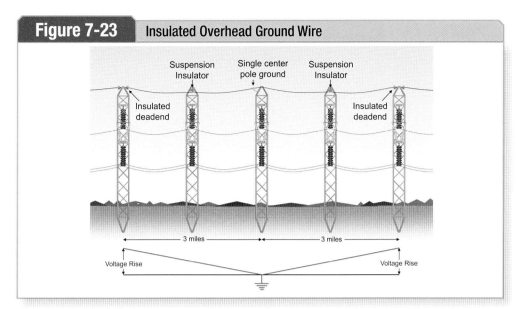

| Figure 7-23 | Insulated Overhead Ground Wire |

Figure 7-23. *Shield wire can be designed and built in interrupted sections several miles in length. It may be insulated and supported by suspension insulators designed to flash over at 2.5 kV. The voltage to earth approaches zero at the ground point, but due to induction and capacitive couplings, the voltage rises as distance to the ground increases. When work is performed on or near a shield wire of this type, a personal protective jumper must be installed at the point of work.*

virtue of its construction and thus is the preferred method. **See Figure 7-21.**

The tower allows a ground for all phases that can be contacted. It may not be necessary to place jumpers on all conductors, but they must be placed on any conductor that can come in contact with a worker or any equipment used by a worker. A ground for at least two phases is needed to operate line protection. It is important to install the ground end first.

When it comes time for removal, always remove the line-connected end first. **See Figure 7-22.**

The preferred method for installing grounds on higher-voltage single-circuit lattice steel transmission line structures, where the conductors are a greater distance from the structure than those on lower-voltage structures, is to install them from the bridge above the conductors.

The overhead shield wires on some EHV transmission circuits are insulated from the individual steel support structures. **See Figure 7-23.** The traditional design for transmission overhead shield wires are terminal-to-terminal continuous conductors grounded at every pole or tower. A departure from this conventional shield is a design that interrupts the whole line continuity by dead-ending and isolating sections about 6 miles in length. These sections are grounded only at mid-point. From the ground point in each direction, the shield wires are insulated from the tower body. Special pin and clevis type suspension insulators support the wires at tangent and deadened structures. These insulators are without skirts and are designed to flash over at 2,500 volts in dry conditions. Shield wires of this type provide overvoltage protection by allowing lightning to easily arc across the cap to pin insulation. The conventional method using a continuous shield wire grounded at each support structure results in circulating currents in every span. Designs with insulated shield wires avoid these circulating currents through the towers, shields, and earth, as in conventional designs. At the center ground point, the voltage on the shield is held to nearly

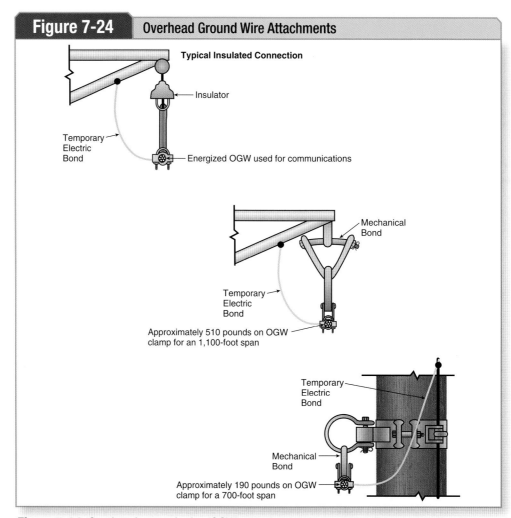

| Figure 7-24 | Overhead Ground Wire Attachments |

Typical Insulated Connection

Insulator

Temporary Electric Bond

Energized OGW used for communications

Mechanical Bond

Temporary Electric Bond

Approximately 510 pounds on OGW clamp for an 1,100-foot span

Temporary Electric Bond

Mechanical Bond

Approximately 190 pounds on OGW clamp for a 700-foot span

Figure 7-24. Overhead ground wire (OGW) attachments vary depending on whether the connection is insulated, for a steel structure, or for a wood pole structure.

earth potential. As the distance from the ground point increases, the shield to earth voltage increases due to electromagnetic and capacitive couplings. If workers approach shield wires of this type, ground cables must be attached. If the line conductors are to be grounded, these shield wires are not to be considered effective grounding electrodes.

Average level span weights do not allow a good electrical connection. **See Figure 7-24.** Fault currents through this hardware can be hazardous; therefore, the connection should be bonded to prevent injury during fault conditions.

On lower-voltage lattice steel transmission lines, grounding the phases from positions on the structure near the level of the conductors may be more

practical and easier than installing grounds from the bridge above the conductors. However, this is not the preferred method. The inductive loop formed by the grounding cable and the structure should be kept to a minimum.

On 230- and 345-kilovolt double-circuit lattice steel transmission structures, workers should ground the phase conductors to the structure arms. Personal protective grounds should be attached from the bottom phase up and removed from the top phase down.

Grounding on deadend or angle lattice steel structures is normally installed on the conductor. **See Figure 7-25.** A deadend loop, sometimes called a jumper, is a metallic wire connecting the conductors on opposite sides of a dead-end structure

Figure 7-25 | Grounding on Steel Deadend Structures

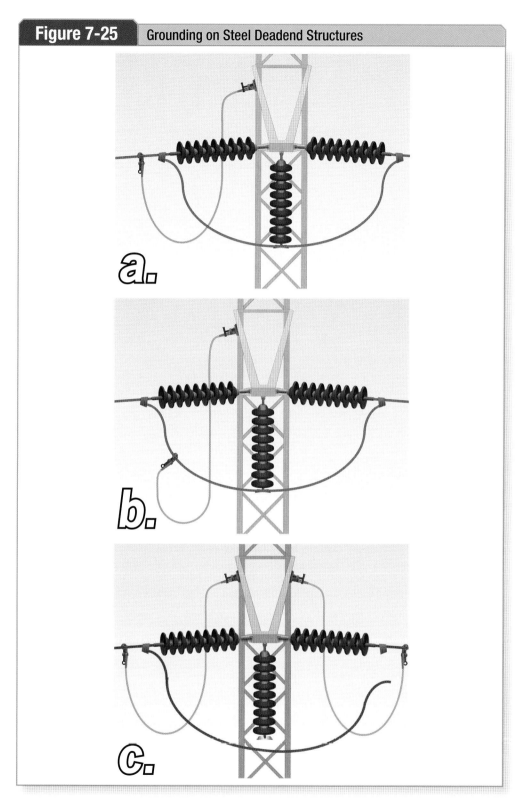

Figure 7-25. *(a) A single ground cable from the tower arm to a tensioned line conductor on either side of the deadend will ground the phase wire at this point of work. (b) Connecting the ground cable to the line jumper is acceptable depending on the work being done. (c) If the jumper is to be disconnected, the conductors (or conductor and jumper) on both sides of the deadends must be grounded.*

Figure 7-26	Splicing on an Insulated Platform

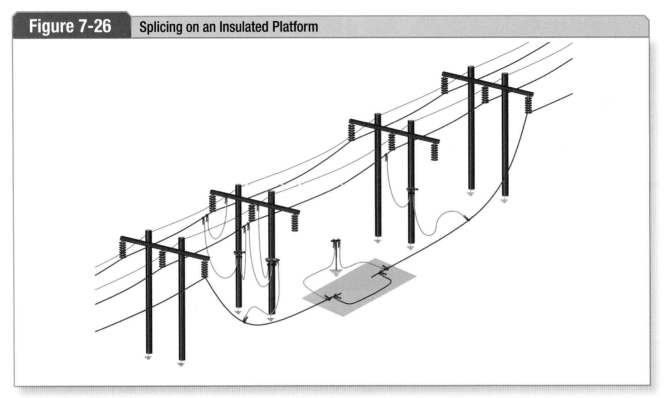

Figure 7-26. Three-phase grounding jumpers with connections to the overhead ground wires are installed at a structure adjacent to the worksite. At the opposite adjacent structure, the single conductor being repaired is grounded. A jumper is installed across the section of damaged conductor using a hot stick. Workers are cautioned to remain on the platform throughout the work process.

so that continuity is maintained. Protective grounds installed by an aerial device may be easier to attach to the structure at conductor level in each case. If the jumper is to be removed or disconnected on either end, the conductor (or conductor and jumper) on both sides of the tension insulator strings is grounded.

Splicing requirements in the next section also pertain to terminating deadends.

Splicing Using Insulated Platforms and Conductive Platforms

Before opening or splicing a deenergized or electrically isolated conductor or overhead ground wire, 3-phase grounding is established at one of the structures from which it is to be worked, detached, or lowered. A single-phase ground is established, for each conductor or overhead ground wire being spliced, at the other structure from which it is to be worked, detached, or lowered.

For a repair, 3-phase grounding is established at the worksite or at the structure nearest to the repair section. If the conductor or overhead ground wire is severed, a single-phase ground is established at the opposite structure on the circuit to be repaired.

A ground is located at each side and within 3 meters (10 feet) of working areas where conductors, subconductors, or overhead ground wire are being spliced. The two ends to be spliced or repaired have a jumper or a section of conductor installed across the damaged or severed section (using a hot stick) to maintain continuity of the conductor or overhead ground wire before cutting a damaged section or connecting a severed section. Continuous grounding must be in place while lowering, splicing, and reinstalling the conductor or overhead ground wire. In other words, the grounds are left in place until the splice is completed.

Figure 7-27   Splicing on a Conductive Mat

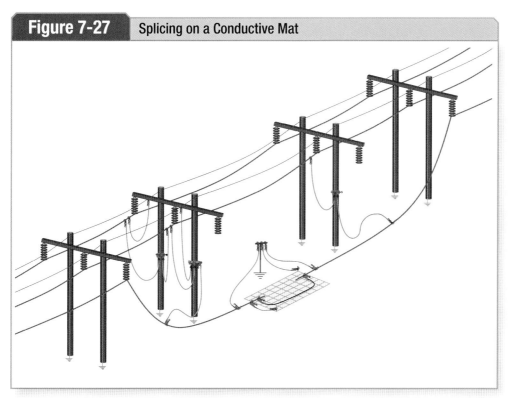

Figure 7-27. *The conductors are cross-phase shortened and connected to the grounded overhead static lines. A jumper placed across the open prevents a potential difference across the conductor ends. Workers will perform the splicing operation from the conductive mat that is bonded to the conductor.*

Splicing is carried out on either an insulated platform or a conductive metallic grounding mat. When a splice is accomplished on the insulated platform, the press and the worker's feet must not extend over the platform or come in contact with earth or the grounded object. **See Figure 7-26.**

When a conductive mat is used, it is recommended that the mat be roped off and an insulated walkway be used to provide access to the mat. The conductor or overhead ground wire must be bonded to the mat grounding rod (perhaps by each end) using a hot stick. **See Figure 7-27.** If a vehicle is involved in the splicing operation, it must be grounded, and a ground cable from the common ground to the conductor or overhead ground wire must be installed with a hot stick. If the splice is to be completed from a vehicle, the vehicle and conductor or overhead ground wire is grounded, and

the workers remain on the vehicle or stand on an insulated platform or metal conductive mat.

The preceding requirements apply to grounding of conductors, subconductors, conductive pulling lines, and overhead ground wires. Requirements not related to protective grounding must be adhered to (that is, barriers, barricading, and crossing guard structures). If fiber-optic leads must be spliced, workers must obtain proper instructions and special tools before beginning the work. Splicing instructions should be obtained from the fiber optics manufacturer.

In some situations, a cable cannot be used to jumper between the severed ends of a conductor or overhead ground wire. The protective 3-phase grounds on the adjacent structures on each side of the separation are adequate for protection from induced currents. To obtain protection from fault currents, insulated platforms should be used at the sock and pulley attachments, and an insulated platform or conductive mat should be used by the winch operator at the winching vehicle. The ground worker pulling the winch line should use an insulating rope or hot stick to avoid contact with the grounded system. An alternate approach is for the worker to stand on an insulated platform or wear properly rated insulated footwear, insulated gloves, or both. The worker should also keep contact time with the grounded system to a minimum.

Summary

A logical series of steps should be followed when installing personal protective grounds. First, the line must be tested for voltage before attempting to apply a protective ground assembly. Next, each connection, including the clamp, needs to be cleaned and then a clamp needs to be applied. The initial connection is made at the ground, and only one conductor should ever be connected per clamp. After this, cable slack should be minimized. Caution is required if the cable is to be "tied off," because cable failure may occur at the tie point. Finally, the connection can be made, following the specific requirements for the project. After the installation has been completed, the assembly can be removed. The specified installation and reverse removal sequence must be followed. For installation, the sequence is ground end, neutral, nearest phase, next-closest phase, farthest phase, and static wire if present; the sequence is reversed to remove the assembly.

Each personal protective grounding assembly is derated when used in parallel combinations to allow for variability in connection placement and unequal resistances. Adjacent (bracket) plus personal protective assemblies may be used when needed, but only after careful study and analysis. An equipotential zone should be used in all cases.

Review Questions

1. Of the several types of instruments available, the voltage tester that provides the most reliable indication of voltage level is the __?__.

    a. MRVD

    b. neon indicator

    c. NVDT

    d. tic tracer

2. Excess grounding cable slack should not be coiled because it creates a __?__.

    a. capacitive coupling

    b. fuse link

    c. high resistance

    d. transformer effect

3. If grounding cables are paralleled, they should have their rating reduced by __?__ if unrestrained.

    a. 10%

    b. 15%

    c. 20%

    d. 25%

4. The use of multiple remote grounds to reduce current at the worksite eliminates the necessity of providing protection at the worksite.

    a. True

    b. False

5. Ground cables installed on crossarm or vertical structures in a(n) __?__ provides the best protection and ensures that the worker cannot be in contact with a conductor more than two jumpers from the cluster bar.

    a. each phase to neutral pattern

    b. neutral to bottom phase arrangement

    c. phase to ground rod to cluster bar arrangement

    d. T configuration

Step and Touch Potential

A review of accident abstracts shows a high frequency of electrical accidents that are related to step and touch potential incidents. The effects of electrical current on the human body depend upon the circuit characteristics (current, voltage, and frequency), contact and internal resistance, current pathway through the body, contact duration, and environmental conditions. Electrical Workers should recognize the common myths regarding earth's conductivity and learn to think of earth as a conductor. This mindset helps ensure proper consideration when designing personal protective grounding schemes.

Objectives

» Understand that the great myth in utility grounding is that a connection to earth is a connection to zero volts.

» Describe the use of isolation as a protective strategy against step and touch potentials.

» Illustrate the use of insulation as a protective strategy against step and touch potentials.

» Relate the use of equipotential zones as a protective strategy against step and touch potentials.

More information available in NJATC Blended Learning: Personal Protective Grounding.

For additional information, visit qr.njatcdb.org
Item #1823

Chapter 8

Table of Contents

Figure 8-1	Step Potential vs Distance

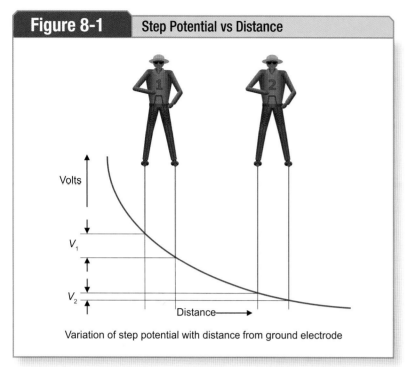

Variation of step potential with distance from ground electrode

Figure 8-1. During a fault current event, the voltage at the earth connection point rises to nearly that of the energized conductor. As the distance from the current entry point increases, the voltage drops off. The voltage curve shows that because Worker 1 is nearer to the ground electrode, the potential difference (V_1) is greater across his contact points than those of Worker 2 (V_2).

Figure 8-2	Decreased Step Potential

Distance (ft)	Voltage (V)
0	40,000
2	20,000
4	10,000
6	5,000
8	2,500
10	1,250
12	620

Figure 8-2. For every 2 to 3 feet, the voltage across earth decreases by about 50%.

EARTH AS A CONDUCTOR

Earth is a conductor. It has resistance and will conduct electricity. Put another way, it resists current and passes current. Thus, it behaves much like a resistor in a circuit.

The voltage at the earth connection rises to equal the line voltage. However, it is not a linear resistance, and contact at the surface does not have a voltage equal to zero volts during fault.

Earth Resistance Defined

The great myth in utility grounding is that a connection to earth is a connection to zero volts, thereby holding the connected point to zero volts. This is only true at a substantial distance from the earth connection point, or away from the point of current entry. Earth has a measurable resistance, like any other circuit resistance; it carries current and develops a voltage drop when current flows through it, just like any other resistor. As the earth path length increases, the current path widens. Resistance is like a wire: with a larger diameter, there is less resistance.

Consider a low-resistance cable connected between an energized conductor and an earth connection point. The voltage at the conductor is almost the same at the earth connection. Only a small voltage drop occurs in the connecting cable. The difference is that the voltage decreases nonlinearly, as opposed to a fixed circuit resistance. This means that as the distance from the current entry point increases, the voltage drops off rapidly. **See Figure 8-1.**

Tests have indicated that as a rule of thumb, at distribution voltages, the drop across earth decreases by about 50% for every two to three feet. An example assumes a 40-kilovolt connection. For this decrease in step potential, the first two feet drop 20 kilovolts, the next two feet drop 10 kilovolts, and so on. **See Figure 8-2.**

The voltage rise curve is used to demonstrate step and touch voltages. **See Figure 8-3.** As the distance from the contact between fault and earth increases, the amount of resistive soil between also increases.

Potential Hazards

Step, touch, and transferred touch potentials, or voltages, occur where there is a difference in potential between two points. These voltages are the result of energization of a grounded conductive object, either by accidental energization (by a fault) or through continuous induced current.

Voltage differences may appear at the worksite because of induction from adjacent circuits, static charge, lightning, or accidental energization. Induction (coupling) is the process of generating time-varying voltages, currents, or both in otherwise-unenergized conductive objects or electrical circuits by the influence of the time-varying fields: electrical, magnetic, or both. If the line, bus, or equipment becomes energized, potentially hazardous voltage differences could result. Protective grounds limit excessive voltage differences in the work area aloft, and proper work procedures reduce exposure to step and touch voltages on the ground.

The most important rule in safe grounding is to ensure that the worker is never in series with a grounding system component. **See Figure 8-4.** Installing protective grounds is considered live work, because a circuit is considered energized until grounded.

Another hazard in the area is the pole guys, which typically are connected directly to an earth anchor and held at zero volts if they lack current flow. If they are connected in any way to any part of the circuit that can become energized during a fault, a step and touch potential is present at the ground level.

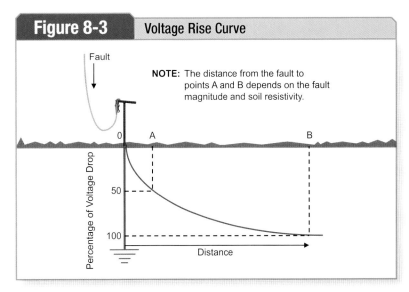

Figure 8-3. Staged fault tests by the Western Area Power Administration show that the voltage rise reaches about 50% of the maximum at 0.5 meter (1 foot 8 inches) to 1.2 meters (3 feet 1 inch) (point A) and near maximum (100%) around 10 meters (32 feet 10 inches) (point B).

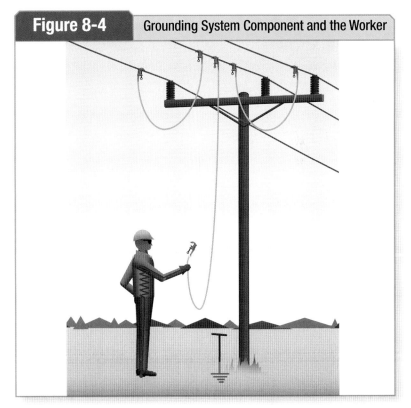

Figure 8-4. Contact with an energized part puts the worker in series with lower-voltage earth, a dangerous situation.

Figure 8-5 | Step Potential

Figure 8-5. The voltage hazard that arises when a voltage is bridged by stepping across a span of earth during current flow is called the step potential or step voltage. More information available in NJATC Blended Learning: Personal Protective Grounding.

For additional information, visit qr.njatcdb.org Item #1823.

UNDERSTANDING STEP POTENTIAL

Step potential or voltage is the potential difference between two points on earth's surface separated by a distance of one pace, which is assumed to be 1 meter (3.3 feet), in the direction of maximum potential gradient. This potential difference could be dangerous when current flows through earth or material upon which the worker is standing, particularly under fault conditions. The closer the worker is to the structure, the higher the earth voltage and thus the higher the step potential.

A worker stepping across the first two-foot span would bridge a much higher voltage than a worker stepping over a similar three-foot span a great distance away. Only a small fraction of the full voltage would be present at the remote distance. Thus, the voltage hazard arises when a voltage is bridged by stepping across a span of earth during current flow. **See Figure 8-5.**

UNDERSTANDING TOUCH POTENTIAL

Touch potential or voltage is the potential difference between a grounded metallic structure and a point on earth's surface separated by a distance equal to a person's normal maximum horizontal reach, approximately one meter (3.3 feet). It is caused by touching an energized part while standing on lower-voltage earth. This potential difference could be dangerous and could result from induction, fault currents, or both. As the worker moves closer to the structure, the earth voltage is higher but the touch voltage is lower—in contrast to step voltage, which increases with rising earth voltage.

A worker is also at risk when standing on remote earth while touching a conductive item that is connected to the higher voltage. **See Figure 8-6.** This transferred touch potential is the voltage difference between points on a surface connected by a conductive element,

Figure 8-6	Remote Earth Risks

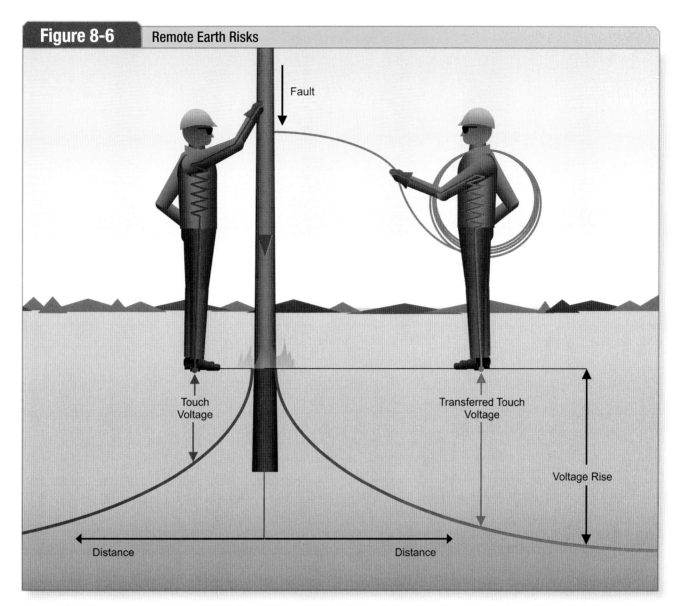

Figure 8-6. Voltage hazard arises from the ability to touch high voltage, directly or indirectly, while standing on a lower voltage. A conductive element may be a tool, cable, vehicle, or any other object capable of transferring a fault. As the distance from the source increases, the voltage across (and thus the body current through) the worker also increases.

which increases the touch voltage greatly as the distance from the source increases. The worker's hands are at the higher voltage, because little voltage drop occurs in the conductive item being touched. The feet are at a lower voltage because the worker is removed from the current entry point.

PROTECTION METHODS AND EQUIPMENT

Both step and touch voltages are hazardous to workers around the base of a structure, trucks, or towers that can become accidentally energized. The protection against these hazards take three forms: isolate, insulate, or develop an equipotential zone. **See Figure 8-7.**

Isolation is accomplished by limiting or restricting the approach distance to grounding systems, such as through barricading or fencing. Barricading is the most efficient way to protect the public from step and touch voltages at a temporary worksite. A barricade is a physical obstruction, such as tapes, cones, or an A-frame–type wood or metal structure, intended to provide a warning about and

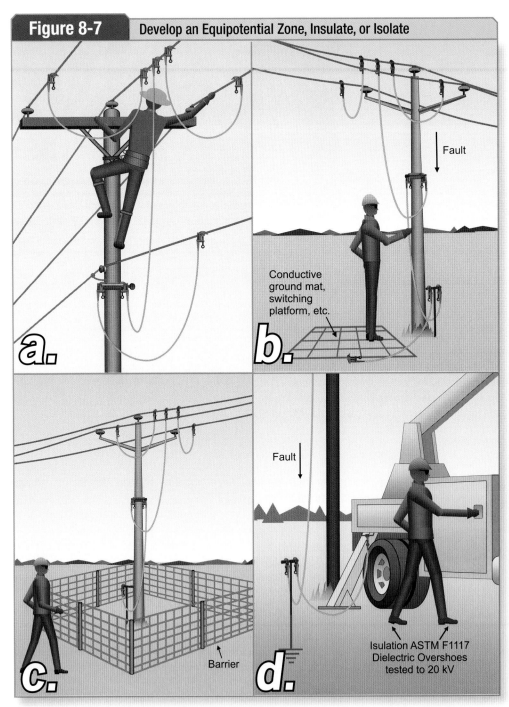

| Figure 8-7 | Develop an Equipotential Zone, Insulate, or Isolate |

a.

b. Conductive ground mat, switching platform, etc.

Fault

c. Barrier

d. Fault

Isulation ASTM F1117 Dielectric Overshoes tested to 20 kV

Figure 8-7. There are three methods of personal protection from hazardous conditions: equipotential aloft (a) and on the ground (b), insulation (c), and isolation (d).

| Figure 8-8 | Insulated Footwear |

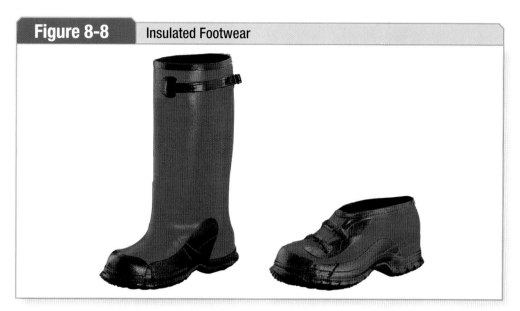

Figure 8-8. The dangers associated with step and touch voltages may be substantially reduced by wearing insulated footwear.

to limit access to a hazardous area. Barricades around truck bodies are a common means of isolation, keeping workers away from any hazardous area. This is not always possible, because it may prevent the needed work from being completed.

Insulation is obtained by using an insulating platform, dielectric footwear, and insulated gloves that are rated for the voltage involved. Requiring the worker to wear rubber-insulating overshoes eliminates the current path of foot–body–foot or hand–body–foot. These overshoes are manufactured in accordance with American Society for Testing and Materials (ASTM) Standard F1117 and tested in accordance with ASTM F1116. As with rubber gloves, attention must be paid to the rating and condition of such overshoes. **See Figure 8-8.**

Equipotential is obtained by keeping the person and reaching activities confined to an equipotential surface. Step potential depends on resistance between the "electrical" ground and the worker on "physical" earth. **See Figure 8-9.** The solution is to create a zone of equipotential for the ground-based worker.

In many cases, it is relatively easy to develop an equipotential zone. Portable ground mats, also known as portable

| Figure 8-9 | Step Potential (Unprotected) |

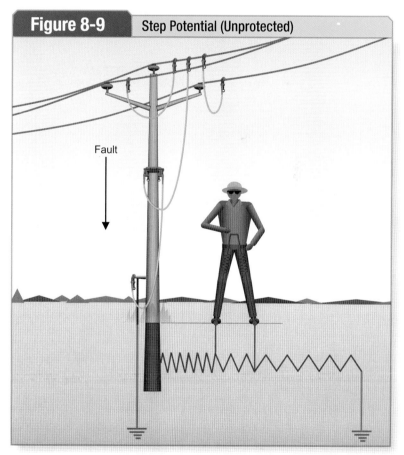

Figure 8-9. Hazardous voltage potential may exist across the worker on the ground.

ground grids, are available for this purpose. **See Figure 8-10.**

Portable ground mats perform the same grid-type function that has been used under both overhead switch-operating handles and substations for many years. They limit hazardous voltage

Figure 8-10 Portable Ground Mats

Figure 8-10. Portable ground mats can be used to develop an equipotential zone.

drop across the person caused by the voltage gradient at the ground site. **See Figure 8-11.**

The mat has conductive braid sufficient to carry a high level of current. It is connected to the object that may become energized. Another jumper that has a high current-carrying capability is connected to the object that may become energized and then connected to the earth or grounding point. The object–mat connection is not intended to carry the full fault current; this is the function of the second connection.

The worker then stands on the mat. The worker is only protected while on the grid or mat. Because the mat is connected to the part that can become energized, the mat is energized to the same voltage. This places the worker's hands and feet at the same voltage, or in an equipotential zone. However, the hazard is not eliminated. It is only moved to the edge of the mat. The first step off of the mat bridges the first two-foot span and the maximum voltage drop.

Portable grids are especially useful around trucks, pad-mounted transformers, and pad-mounted switches. The mats can be connected together to increase the protective area upon which

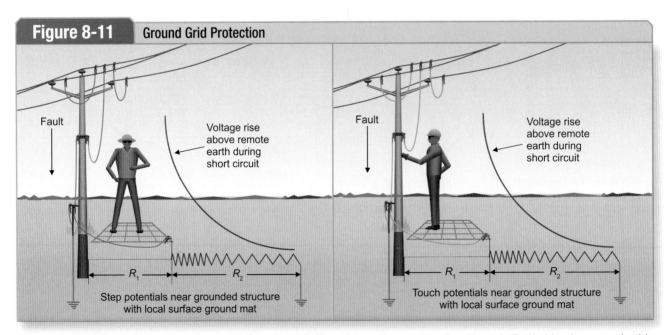

Figure 8-11   Ground Grid Protection

Fault

Voltage rise above remote earth during short circuit

R_1 R_2

Step potentials near grounded structure with local surface ground mat

Fault

Voltage rise above remote earth during short circuit

R_1 R_2

Touch potentials near grounded structure with local surface ground mat

Figure 8-11. Voltage drop across the ground worker, whether step voltage or touch voltage, is limited by the ground grid.

Figure 8-12	Minimum Approach Distance			
Phase-to-Phase Voltage (in kilovolts)	**Distance to Worker**			
	Phase to Ground		**Phase to Phase**	
	(in meters)	(in feet)	(in meters)	(in feet)
0.50–0.300[2]	Avoid contact		Avoid contact	
0.301–0.750[2]	0.33	1.09	0.33	1.09
0.751–5.0	0.63	2.07	0.63	2.07
5.1–15.0	0.65	2.14	0.68	2.24
15.1–36.0	0.77	2.53	0.89	2.92
36.1–46.0	0.84	2.76	0.98	3.22
46.1–72.5	1.00	3.29	1.20	3.94
72.6–121.0	1.13	3.71	1.42	4.66
121.1–145.0	1.30	4.27	1.64	5.38
145.1–169.0	1.46	4.79	1.94	6.36
169.1–242.0	2.01	6.59	3.08	10.10
242.1–362.0	3.41	11.19	5.52	18.11
362.1–420.0	4.25	13.94	6.81	22.34
420.1–550.0	5.07	16.63	8.24	27.03
550.1–800.0	6.88	22.57	11.38	37.34

For additional information, visit qr.njatcdb.org
Item #1795

Figure 8-12. Minimum approach distances for electrical workers are set out in the National Electrical Safety Code.

a worker may stand. They can also be used in some underground distribution functions.

To minimize the exposure to hazardous levels of step, touch, and transferred touch voltages on transmission line systems, people not involved in the work activity should stay a minimum of three meters (10 feet) from the grounding system (structures, vehicles, guy wires, and ground rods). The minimum distance may increase with new system designs with greater fault capability.

Electrical workers may approach energized circuits up to the minimum approach distances in accordance with the 2012 edition of the *National Electrical Safety Code*. The Institute of Electrical and Electronics Engineers also offers a guideline for minimum approach distances for energized lines. **See Figure 8-12.**

The altitude correction factors are applied to these distances in accordance with the *National Electrical Safety Code*. **See Figure 8-13.**

Figure 8-13	Correction Factors Based on Altitude		
Altitude		**Correction Factor**	
(in meters)	(in feet)		
900	3,000	1.00	
1,200	4,000	1.02	
1,500	5,000	1.05	
1,800	6,000	1.08	
2,100	7,000	1.11	
2,400	8,000	1.14	
2,700	9,000	1.17	
3,000	10,000	1.20	
3,600	12,000	1.25	

Figure 8-13. Altitude correction factors must be applied to minimum approach distances to ensure worker safety.

Before coming within the minimum approach distance of circuits or equipment to be grounded, workers should obtain a clearance, electrically isolate the circuit or equipment, remove all power sources from the circuit or equipment, and test for voltage. Protective ground cables may then be applied while maintaining the minimum approach distance from adjacent energized circuits.

Nonelectrical workers must comply with a separate, larger set of minimum approach distances in accordance with the *National Electrical Safety Code*. **See Figure 8-14.**

Acceptable methods are available for installing protective ground cables while maintaining the minimum approach distances. **See Figure 8-15.** All circuits and equipment are treated as energized until tested and properly grounded.

Figure 8-14	Nonelectrical Worker Minimum Approach Distances		
Phase-to-Phase Voltage (in kilovolts)	**Electrical Phase-to-Ground Distance**		
	(in meters)	**(in feet and inches)**	
0.751–90.0	3.05	10-0	
91–121	3.26	10-8	
138–145	3.46	11-4	
161–169	3.56	11-8	
230–242	3.97	13-0	
345–362	4.68	15-4	
500–550	5.80	19-0	
765–800	7.32	24-0	

Figure 8-14. Minimum approach distances for nonelectrical workers are greater than those for electrical workers.

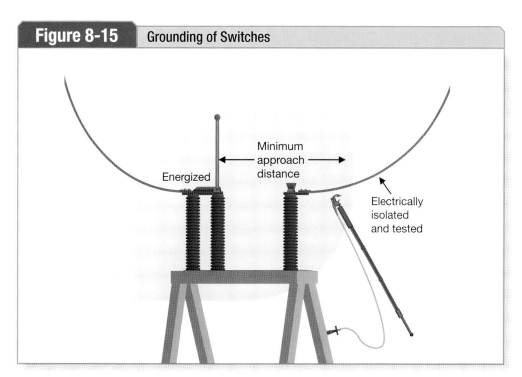

Figure 8-15 | Grounding of Switches

Minimum approach distance

Energized

Electrically isolated and tested

Figure 8-15. When attaching a ground cable to the de-energized side of an open switch, minimum approach distances to all energized surfaces must be maintained.

Summary

An earth path behaves like a nonlinear resistor: it resists current and passes current. Step potential the possible difference between two points about one meter apart on earth's surface, and it can be dangerous when current flows underneath a worker's feet. In contrast to step potential, touch potential is a remote hazard. This difference between a grounded metallic structure and a point on earth's surface is also separated by about one meter.

Like any resistor, earth develops a voltage drop when current flows through it, and the voltage drop across earth decreases fairly quickly. The highest voltage that can be stepped across is at earth's point of current entry.

There are three methods of protection from either step or touch potential: isolation, insulation, and equipotential zone. A worksite can be isolated using barricading or fencing, a worker can be insulated by protective equipment, or an equipotential zone can be created by keeping the worker and all reaching activities within an equipotential surface. However, such solutions are only effective when used correctly. For example, a ground grid or portable mat offers protection only while the worker remains on the mat.

Review Questions

1. At distribution voltages, for every two or three feet from the earth's current entry point, the voltage decreases by about __?__.
   a. 35%
   b. 50%
   c. 65%
   d. 80%

2. When fault current flows to earth, the step potential risk to a worker is __?__ as the distance from the earth entry point increases.
   a. amplified
   b. raised
   c. reduced
   d. unchanged

3. A worker touching an energized steel pole at arm reach while standing on lower-voltage earth is subject to touch potential difference. If another worker standing six feet away is touching the energized pole with a conductive object, the transferred touch potential across this person will be __?__ that of the first worker.
   a. equal to
   b. greater than
   c. less than
   d. similar to

4. Workers wearing voltage rated rubber insulating overshoes are not protected from __?__ body current paths.
   a. foot-to-foot
   b. hand-to-hand
   c. hand-to-foot
   d. head-to-foot

5. Workers stepping on and off of portable conductive mats are within an equipotential zone and are protected from step potentials.
   a. True
   b. False

Induced Voltage and Multiple Grounds

The most common electrical accident, other than direct contact with energized lines, is that of induction and the use of multiple grounds. A line that has been deenergized and isolated is subject to induced voltage often caused by wind or nearby energized lines. This is especially common at transmission voltage levels, where multiple circuits share common structures or rights-of-way for many miles. Capacitive coupling and electromagnetic coupling may exist. The most serious induced voltage comes from an adjacent energized line carrying current. The causes and effects of induced voltages can lead to serious problems which must be addressed at every on-site job briefing. The chapter uses a case study to illustrate the dangers and hazards of induced voltages and multiple grounds.

Objectives

» Explain why induced voltage is a primary cause of accidents.

» Understand why multiple grounds place multiple contact points at different voltages.

» Recognize that induced voltage and current are not limited to line conductors.

Chapter 9

Table of Contents

INDUCTION

Induction is the most common cause of accidents. Induction generates time-varying voltages, currents, or both in otherwise-unenergized conductive objects or electrical circuits. The greater the common distance, the greater the induced voltage or current. In addition, the higher the line above earth, the higher the induced voltage.

A current is electrically isolated, or deenergized, when all load current interrupting devices have been opened on a deenergized electrical circuit or equipment. These interrupting devices include switches, disconnectors, jumpers, taps, or other means through which known sources of electrical energy may be supplied to the particular lines and equipment.

Although it is not the most common cause of accidents, accidental reenergizing of "dead" lines can occur. Therefore, grounds have to be sized and selected to carry the maximum fault current that may be available at all worksites where they will be used.

Causes and Effects of Induced Voltage

A line that has been deenergized and isolated is subject to induced voltage. Three forms of induced voltage may be present:

- Static charge caused by wind or atmospheric source
- Capacitive coupling, in which isolated lines and earth form capacitors
- Electromagnetic coupling induced from current flow in adjacent lines

Induced voltage is often caused by wind or nearby energized lines. Both capacitive coupling and electromagnetic coupling are especially common at transmission voltage levels, where multiple circuits share common structures or rights-of-way for many miles.

When electrical circuits are in close proximity to each other, there exists the

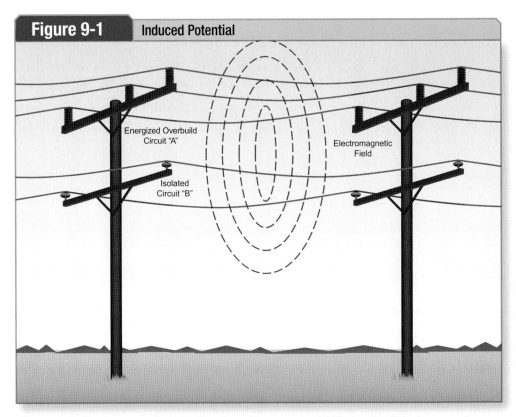

Figure 9-1 | **Induced Potential**

Energized Overbuild Circuit "A"

Isolated Circuit "B"

Electromagnetic Field

Figure 9-1. *Electromagnetic induction from the energized "A" circuit will induce a voltage or potential in the isolated "B" circuit.*

possibility that one circuit may "induce" a charge or "potential" or an electrical "pressure" into the adjacent circuit. Two possible ways that an adjacent or proximate conductor or circuit may be energized is as a result of either "electrostatic" or "electromagnetic" induction. Electrostatic induction is a method to create or generate a charge in a material by bringing an electrically charged object near it or by bringing it close to an object of a lesser or no charge. In the case of adjacent power line circuits, if circuit "A" is energized at a given potential, an electrical "field" will exist around that conductor. If circuit "A" is energized but is not feeding a load or source, the field around the conductor will be a "voltage" field.

If circuit "A" is feeding a load or source, the voltage field around the conductor will diminish and a current or electromagnetic field will develop around the conductor. This action is due to the fact that voltage and amperage are "inversely proportional." In other words, as one field increases the other decreases.

If a conductive object (circuit "B") is in close proximity to an object, such as one power line circuit close to another power line circuit, and one circuit has either a voltage or current field around it, then that field will induce a charge or "potential" in the adjacent or proximate conductive object (circuit). **See Figure 9-1.**

The air capacitance between the energized line and the isolated line couples voltage to the isolated one. Capacitive current is also coupled from the energized line and the isolated line to earth below. Capacitive induced currents of 2 to 10 milliamperes that flow between the lines and to earth are common.

The two lines form the two plates of the capacitor. The dielectric component is air. The closer the lines, the greater the charge buildup on the deenergized line. It may even approach the energized line value. **See Figure 9-2.**

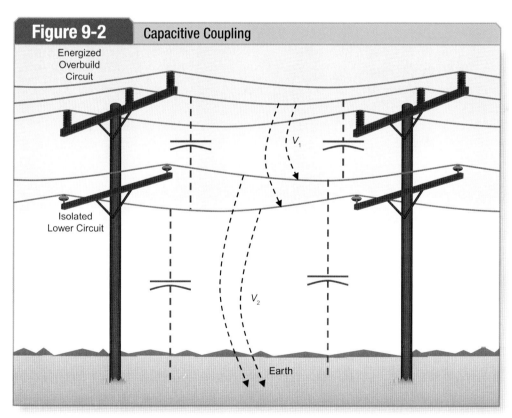

Figure 9-2 | Capacitive Coupling

Energized Overbuild Circuit

V_1

Isolated Lower Circuit

V_2

Earth

Figure 9-2. Energized and isolated circuit act as capacitor plates with air being the separation dielectric. A capacitive coupling exists between the circuits. The earth also serves as a plate providing line to ground capacitor coupling. These capacitors cause an electrical charge to build on the isolated line.

Measurements on isolated Western Area Power Administration, Sierra Nevada, lines give examples of capacitive-coupled voltages and currents. **See Figure 9-3.**

When the isolated line has only a single earth connection, the voltage approaches 0 volts at that point as soon as the first ground is installed. This transfers the hazard to a new location. The voltage rises as the distance from this connection point increases, up to the maximum induced level that can be achieved. A maximum induced voltage may be seen at the end of the line. **See Figure 9-4.**

A more serious induced voltage comes from an adjacent energized line carrying current. With electromagnetic-coupled lines, the magnetic field of the energized line couples to the isolated line, forming an air core transformer with a one-to-one ratio. When the isolated line has only a single earth connection, the voltage approaches zero volts at the grounded point. **See Figure 9-4.** This voltage increases away from the earth connection point to a steady charging current of 10 to 20 milliamperes.

Maximum voltage appears at the open end of the electromagnetic-coupled line. The full coupled voltage returns instantly as the final ground is removed. A large arc may occur when placing or removing grounds.

Understanding Induced Voltage

Induced voltage and current are not limited to line conductors. In some cases, the induced voltage may be felt when mounting onto steel structures. This is a form of step potential. Tower steel may be "hot" when installed in high-resistance soil. The tower becomes energized by induction, and earth two feet away is at a lower voltage. Thus, tower voltage should be measured. Hazardous step and touch voltages may exist, so the tower should be mounted using an insulated mat.

Transmission line terminal ground switches can help ensure that the protective devices (relays, circuit breakers, or fuses) operate within the given time-current relationship to isolate the source of accidental electrical energization. However, depending on the system configuration and loading conditions, the closing of terminal ground switches can increase circulating induced current, causing hazardous levels of step and touch voltage. The ground switches are mainly used to allow application of personal protective grounds where the transmission line is subjected to high induced voltages. They are not used in lieu of personal protective ground cables.

With low or no induced voltage, transmission line terminal ground switches may be used at the discretion of the crew. They do provide protection against accidental reclosures.

Figure 9-3	Isolated Western Area Power Administration Lines	
Name	**Type**	**Voltage** (in volts)
Tracy–Contra line	69-kV line	6,170
Tracy switchyard	69-kV bus	2,000
Keswick–Elverta line	69-kV line	3,350

Figure 9-3. Voltages were measured for actual capacitive-coupled lines.

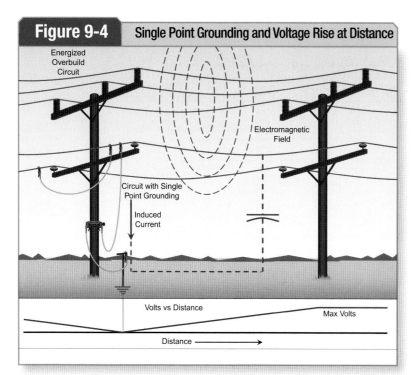

Figure 9-4 | Single Point Grounding and Voltage Rise at Distance

Figure 9-4. At the grounding location, the single point method holds the voltage to neutral or earth at equal potential. Because of electromagnetic and capacitive coupling, the voltage increases to maximum value as distance from the ground point increases.

At high induced voltage, if personal protective ground arcing is unacceptable while attempting conductor contact with the transmission line terminal ground switches open, the switches should be closed and application of the grounding cables should be completed. Transmission line terminal ground switches are then opened to reduce ground-circulating current at the worksite. On transmission lines, the area is normally in the vicinity of a structure.

Very high induced voltage occurs close to transmission lines that are heavily loaded (usually 500-kilovolt lines). When the induced voltage is very high, it becomes difficult or even impossible to install personal protective grounds due to excessive arcing. In these cases, the work method depends on the transferred touch voltages at the worksite and is chosen in accordance with the job hazard analysis. This measurement only needs to be made and documented once, unless significant system changes occur.

Heavily loaded parallel circuits transfer induced current onto the line being worked. Depending on magnitude of the induced current and the work location on the line, the induced charge on capacitors and reactors may create situations in which it is difficult or impossible to install protective grounds. In these situations, capacitors and reactors on the transmission line being worked should be removed from the circuit before installing the grounding cables.

MULTIPLE GROUNDS

A problem more serious than induction comes when a second jumper is placed on the isolated and deenergized line. A complete circuit is thus formed, and depending upon the voltage and earth resistance, current will flow. Because earth acts as a resistive conductor, this earth resistance limits the current level.

When the isolated line has multiple grounds, multiple current loops are formed. Again, the earth resistance, number of loops, and magnetic strength of the energized line limit the induced current. This current may be on the order of a few amperes to hundreds of amperes. It can be hazardous to both

workers aloft and workers on the ground. **See Figure 9-5.**

Extreme voltage current may be induced in completed circuits. **See Figure 9-6.**

Hazards of Multiple Grounds

As part of a protection scheme, use of separate grounds may be hazardous. This usage often results in serious accidents and fatalities and can be especially hazardous when trucks are involved.

The following scenario may be fatal: The truck is using a separate, remote ground,

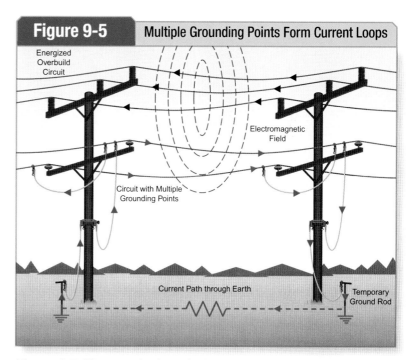

Figure 9-5. The energized overbuilt circuit creates an electromagnetic field. A cutting action from that field induces a voltage into the isolated bottom circuit. When a second grounding set is installed on the line, a closed circuit is formed, resulting in an induced current flow through the ground cables, line, and earth.

Figure 9-6	Induced Voltages and Currents of Completed Circuits		
Name	**Type**	**Voltage (in volts)**	**Current (in amperes)**
Tracy–Contra line	69-kV line	600	49
Keswick–Elverta line	230-kV line	716	17

Figure 9-6. Induced voltages and currents of completed circuits were measured on isolated Western Area Power Administration, Sierra Nevada, lines.

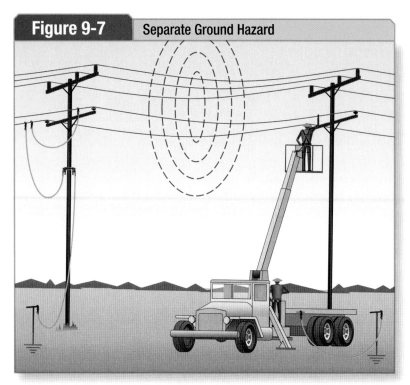

Figure 9-7. *The truck is grounded at a distance from the line ground location. The worker in contact with the line is in a non-insulated man basket. A potential difference exists between the two grounding points and the worker between these grounding points is at risk. The current pathway through the worker, boom, truck chassis, and temporary grounding equipment can be lethal.*

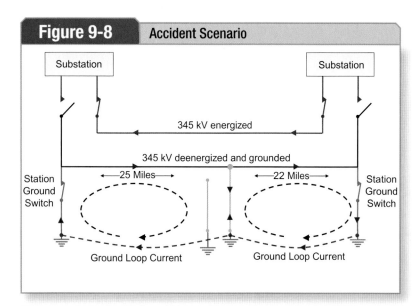

Figure 9-8. *In December 2000, a fatal accident occurred while repairs were being made to a 345 kV line in a shared right-of-way. Improper grounding procedures were determined to be the chief cause.*

which is set away from the line ground. The risk occurs when the line ground is at high voltage, the truck ground is at low voltage, and the worker is between the two grounds. **See Figure 9-7.**

Understanding Multiple Grounds

Often the problem of multiple grounds is encountered while using trucks during maintenance work. For example, if a worker in a manned basket on a metal boom is grounded, the worker becomes a path to earth as soon as contact is made to a conductor. Even with the presence of other protective grounds on adjacent structures, the worker presents an additional path. Often the ground is placed a distance from the truck. This remote ground ensures the truck body remains near zero volts, maximizing the voltage drop across the contacting worker.

Such a fatality involving an experienced worker occurred in the New England area in 2000. The top of a tangent wood structure, containing a 345-kilovolt conductor, had broken off. The broken part was hanging by a static wire. The damaged pole was part of a 3-phase, 345-kilovolt line that shared a common right-of-way corridor with another 3-phase, 345-kilovolt line for 47 miles. The worksite was approximately midpoint of the shared corridor. The damaged pole held the conductor closest to the energized line. The undamaged line remained energized during the repairs. **See Figure 9-8.**

When the damaged line was deenergized, both ends were grounded with station ground switches at the substations. These closed grounding switches created a 47-mile long air core transformer. The induced current flow through the grounded conductors returned through the earth creating a continuous current loop. A grounding set was installed on a structure three spans from the work site. This midpoint conductor ground resulted in creating two complete ground loop circuits. The truck used to lift the workers had a steel boom and was grounded to the pole ground of the center pole of the deenergized line. The static wires were bonded and connected to earth at a location one span from the truck. **See Figure 9-9.**

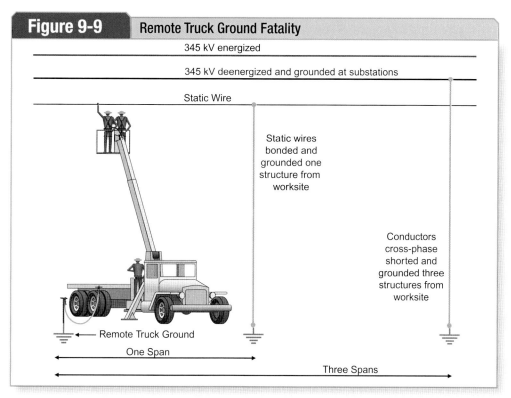

Figure 9-9	Remote Truck Ground Fatality

345 kV energized

345 kV deenergized and grounded at substations

Static Wire

Static wires bonded and grounded one structure from worksite

Conductors cross-phase shorted and grounded three structures from worksite

Remote Truck Ground

One Span

Three Spans

Figure 9-9. Two men were working from a man basket attached to the boom of a truck crane. The truck chassis was grounded some distance from the static line ground point. Before contact, a potential difference of 300 volts existed between the static line and the workers. When a worker made contact, the body current caused muscle contraction and ultimately the death of that worker.

The workers had worked nearly all day to complete the repairs. A new pole had been set, and the conductor had been placed on the new pole. There had been no indication of voltage present, such as arcing or tingling during the repairs.

When the repairs were nearly complete, the worker was in the process of relocating the static wire from the temporary position on the center pole to the new pole. Throughout the repair, he had been wearing only worn leather gloves. At this point, the worker removed his leather gloves and grabbed the static wire while holding onto the platform rail. He let out a gasp and dropped to the bottom of the bucket. The coworker in the bucket had to pry his fingers from the static wire, one by one. It was determined that his death was due to low-voltage electrocution. The body current was above the "let-go" level and sufficient to cause his death.

It was later found that the voltage between the grounded platform rail and the static wire, without any connection, was 300 volts. The leather gloves apparently had provided sufficient insulation to protect the workers. It was also determined that if an equipotential jumper had been placed between the platform and the static wire, the voltage would have been limited to 0.5 volt, a harmless level.

Thus, the induction fatality was caused by

- Induced voltage
- The use of separate grounds for the truck and the personal protective ground
- The worker's failure to test the line for voltage
- The worker's removal of his leather gloves

Better training could have avoided this fatality.

Summary

Induced voltage is a primary cause of accidents, some fatal. It occurs in three forms: static charge, capacitive coupling, and electromagnetic coupling. Electromagnetic induction causes current to flow in circuits completed by earth paths.

Multiple grounds place multiple contact points at different voltages, completing a circuit and allowing induced current to flow at a worksite. Such a system can be hazardous, particularly to workers in the bucket of a truck with a steel boom. Potential voltage differences caused by multiple remote grounds can even be fatal.

Review Questions

1. **Which one of the following is not a form of induced voltage?**

    a. Accidental reenergization

    b. Capacitive coupling

    c. Electromagnetic coupling

    d. Static Charge

2. **Wind can cause an induced voltage in the form of a(n) ? .**

    a. capacitive coupling

    b. electromagnetic coupling

    c. mutual inductance

    d. static charge

3. **The single point grounding method holds the line to neutral or earth voltage at an equal potential at the grounding site. As distance from the ground site is increased, the line to earth voltage ? .**

    a. decreases

    b. increases

    c. is held at zero

    d. remains the same

4. **The cutting action of the electromagnetic field from an energized line induces a voltage in an adjacent isolated line. A closed circuit current loop is formed when ? .**

    a. a second grounding point is established

    b. the first ground set is installed

    c. substation grounding switches are opened

    d. trucks and equipment are bonded to the line

5. **With protective grounds installed on an adjacent structure, a worker in a crane mounted uninsulated man basket is safe to contact the line if the ? .**

    a. distance from the adjacent structure ground point is less than 500 feet

    b. substation ground switches are closed

    c. truck chassis is grounded and the basket is bonded to the line

    d. truck chassis is grounded to a temporary ground rod

Truck Grounding

Frequently, jobsite conditions warrant working from or around trucks and aerial lifts of various types. Fortunately, many of the standard personal protection principles can be applied. The challenge is applying these principles to various worksite conditions and different job scenarios.

A truck is often grounded through a driven ground rod. This ensures that a faulted line sees sufficient current to operate the line's protective equipment. It does not provide safety to a worker around the truck. Protection of the worker around these vehicles is the paramount concern.

Objectives

» Learn how workers at ground level around a truck can be protected from both step and touch voltage hazards.

» Apply personal protective grounding strategies to grounding of metal boom devices.

» Apply personal protective grounding strategies to grounding of insulated boom devices.

Chapter 10

Table of Contents

TYPES OF AERIAL DEVICES

Working around or from aerial devices presents several personal protection problems. The variety of the needed protection situations arise from the numerous types and configurations of trucks and the many manners in which they are used. Regardless, all standard means of worker protection can be employed.

Some devices in service have conductive metal booms; others have insulated booms. **See Figure 10-1.** Some of those with insulated booms have short insulated sections in the lower steel boom; others do not.

Some devices have the operator standing on the truck; for others, the operator must stand on the ground during operation. **See Figure 10-2.** Most trucks have storage compartments holding tools and supplies that must be accessed by ground workers.

| Figure 10-1 | Insulated and Conductive Truck Booms |

Figure 10-1. Certain jobs may utilize trucks with an assortment of boom types. The digger derrick on the left has two telescoping sections. The hydraulic section is constructed of fiberglass with dielectric properties. The removable jib is also fiberglass. The hydraulic crane on the right has an all-steel conductive boom. The workers in the bucket are protected by the fiberglass bucket and also by insulated upper and lower boom sections.

Metal Boom Devices

The workers on an elevated platform can become a path to earth upon contact with a conductor, neutral, or static wire that has voltage present. Nearly the full voltage would be developed across the worker that first contacts the conductor from the basket. No voltage drop occurs across a resistor until there is current flow through it and both ends of the resistor are at the same voltage. When the truck makes intimate contact with earth and no current is flowing through the truck, the boom tip remains near the zero volts of earth. If the line has voltage, because it is energized or from induction, the voltage across the open-air gap formed by the worker to the line is the maximum present and available. Because the resistance of the worker is generally so much greater than both the truck and earth as a return path, this voltage is across the worker's body as soon as contact is made. It is essential that the line be tested to ensure that there is no voltage present before proceeding.

Insulated Boom Devices

The workers on an elevated platform with boom insulation do not become a path to earth upon contact with a conductor, neutral, or static wire that has voltage present. They may be

| Figure 10-2 | Boom Truck Operated from Ground |

Figure 10-2. Some line trucks require the operator to stand on the ground during operation.

subjected to body-induced voltage if a nearby line is energized. There would be some low-current arcing upon contact, but the current would be on the order of microamperes and would stop when the platform, workers, and conductor are bonded to the same voltage. **See Figure 10-3.**

WORKER PROTECTION IN AERIAL DEVICES

Protective methods for truck grounding are the same as those applied to other types of protective grounding. An equipotential zone should be developed for any worker in contact with the truck. The use of barricades lowers the risk of step and touch hazards by keeping all nonessential workers away from the truck.

Vehicles involved in maintenance activities are grounded as the first step in establishing a grounding system. Vehicle grounding is a form of protective grounding. The vehicle is grounded, or connected, to earth or to a grounding system by means of a portable cable assembly designed to carry the maximum anticipated fault current and anticipated continuous current at the worksite. Aerial devices, whether with an insulated or uninsulated boom, and other maintenance vehicles that may contact a grounded system are grounded to that system. Vehicles situated such that a worker can contact them simultaneously are bonded to a common ground. A hot stick is used to install and remove vehicle grounds on a grounded system bonded to a conductor, bus, or piece of equipment.

Ground cables on reels or looped on the vehicle are completely unwound to eliminate destructive forces resulting from induction. When grounding vehicles with permanently mounted reel-type grounding cables, it is permissible to bond the ground cable to the structure ground or to a ground rod. If there is a potential for hazardous induced voltages

on the vehicle, a hot stick should be used to attach the grounding cable.

Barricades, Insulation, and Establishing an Equipotential Zone

With trucks, the worker protection available includes barricades, insulation, and the establishment of an equipotential

| Figure 10-3 | Aerial Devices with Boom Insulation |

Figure 10-3. Boom insulation protects workers on elevated platforms.

zone, each at a different location on or around the truck. **See Figure 10-4.**

In many situations, the spacing of the conductors creates a hazard to the worker aloft. Nearby lines should be covered with insulating materials, or an equipotential zone should be established for worker protection. This is appropriate

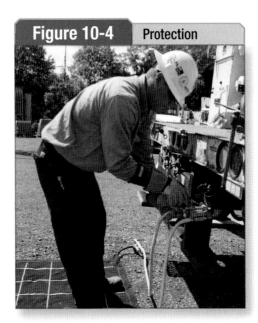

Figure 10-4. *Protection for ground personnel must always be a consideration during the on-site job briefing.*

Figure 10-5. *Workers leaving a bonded truck must step onto a protective mat to avoid step potential hazards.*

for use from both insulated and conductive boom aerial lifts. The hazard to the worker aloft may be line to line, line to neutral, or line to a grounded part.

Whenever possible, vehicles should be grounded to a structure or piece of equipment. When grounding to the structure is not practical, such as during midspan work, the vehicle is grounded to a ground rod installed near the midpoint and as close to the vehicle as practical. This driven ground rod ensures that a faulted line sees sufficient current to operate the line's protective equipment. It does not provide safety to a worker around the truck. If the body becomes energized, the voltage is transferred to all direct earth contacts—that is, to the outrigger feet (if not on insulating wood slabs), to the tire contacts, and to the driven ground. As the distance from these contact points increases, the touch potential increases. Testing done for Puget Sound Power and Light measured equipotential zone voltages if the worker stood immediately adjacent to an outrigger. However, lethal voltages were measured if the worker stood at the front or rear of the truck.

If grounding of the vehicle or vehicles is not possible, the operator should remain on the vehicle, on an insulated platform, or on a conductive mat that is bonded to the vehicle. Vehicles with conductive winch lines in contact with a grounding system should be equipped with an insulated platform or conductive mat for the winch operator to stand on. No one should approach within three meters (10 feet) of a grounded vehicle while it is in contact with a conductor, bus, or other grounded equipment.

Capacitive-coupled voltage on the body of an ungrounded truck may be present. A single ground from the truck to earth provides a discharge path for this induced voltage. The earth connection may complete a current circuit for electromagnetic induction. If this is the case, there may be step, touch, or both potential hazards around every earth contact point and from earth to the truck body. This is especially hazardous during an accidental reenergization. The worker on the ground near the truck is usually the one injured or killed. **See Figure 10-5.**

Ground workers should stay clear—at least three meters (10 feet) where feasible—of items such as down guys, ground rods, maintenance vehicles, and structure legs or ground wires while they are bonded to protective grounds that are in place. When it is necessary to work on or near these features, workers should use bonded conductive or insulated platforms or approved insulated footwear to minimize the hazards from step and touch voltages.

Personal Protective Grounding with Metal Boom Devices

An uninsulated truck uses a common ground point to avoid a difference of potential between grounds. Without current flow, there is no voltage drop. Thus, a worker in a conductive bucket is at zero volts before contacting the conductor. **See Figure 10-6.**

The truck and line should be kept at the same voltage in case of accidentally energized or induced voltages, which presents a step potential hazard. The line should be tested; personal insulation should be used until the line condition is confirmed.

Noninsulated aerial devices should be

Figure 10-6. Uninsulated trucks are grounded from a common point.

bonded to the conductor to eliminate multiple current paths and potential differences during fault conditions. Metal liners in buckets should be removed or bonded to the grounded system. **See Figure 10-7.**

Protection for the elevated worker can be from the use of insulation (rubber gloves and cover-ups) or the establishment of an equipotential zone. A low-resistance bypass jumper from the conductor to the basket or boom forms an equipotential zone.

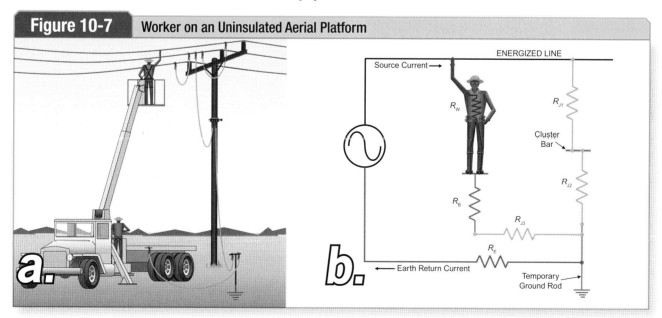

Figure 10-7. (a) The conductive boom, platform, and line conductors are bonded to a common earth electrode. (b) The jumpers from the lines to the ground rod (R_{J1} and R_{J2}) provide a low resistance path in parallel with the worker (R_W) and aerial platform (R_B).

Figure 10-8 — Installing Personal Grounds from a Bucket

Figure 10-8. *The same safe work procedures used when grounding from a pole are necessary when the task is done from a bucket. The cluster bar has cables attached to both the center phase and neutral. As an additional precaution, another cable can be connected from the cluster bar to a temporary ground rod.*

Figure 10-9 — Steel Conductive Boom and an Energized Line

Figure 10-9. *Extreme caution must be taken when conductive booms are in the proximity of energized lines. Arcing, extreme fault currents, and step potential hazards will result if boom to line contact is made.*

Grounding cluster bars should be used on all poles of wood structures. **See Figure 10-8.**

During maintenance work, a common ground should be used for the truck, the line, and a driven ground. This common connection keeps the voltage the same on all components. While the jumper protects the workers aloft if the line becomes accidentally reenergized, the hazard is transferred to the ground workers and additional protection must be used.

Workers at ground level are subject to nuisance shocks from capacitive-coupled voltage from nearby energized lines. A single driven ground reduces or eliminates the induced voltage on the truck body. This ground may also allow sufficient fault current to flow if accidentally reenergized. It is important to operate on the lines while using protective equipment and to minimize the time the fault current flows.

Contacting an energized line with a conductive steel boom has been the cause of many accidents to personnel standing on the ground and touching the truck during this contact. **See Figure 10-9.** Ground workers are also subject to step and touch potentials around the truck from induced voltages. Touch potential protection for ground workers is mandatory at the truck site. The worker on the truck is normally not at risk of touch potential.

Portable ground mats connected to the truck body can be used to develop an equipotential zone for ground workers. **See Figure 10-10.** They must remain on the mats and not step off; otherwise, from that first step, they would bridge the greatest voltage present. An additional connection to carry the fault current must be made; the mat connection should not be the trip current path.

Barricading the truck to prevent worker contact during the time the boom is elevated is a common protection method. Although it is effective, barricading is often inconvenient, because the barricade must be lowered each time to retrieve tools or supplies stored on the truck.

A series of Puget Sound Power and Light tests were conducted on a metal boom line truck. The tests indicated the following:

- Boom tip to body resistance was in the range of 2 to 3 ohms.
- An equipotential zone must be established for a worker immediately adjacent to an outrigger in contact with earth.
- A fatal voltage would develop across a worker contacting either the front or the rear of the truck if a line was accidentally reenergized.

In the first test on an ungrounded truck, the line was energized to 7.2 kilovolts in a set of five tests. The worker making contact with the front or rear of the truck encountered a voltage of 5,307 to 5,856 volts and a current of 5.8 to 6.3 amperes.

In the second test, the truck was grounded to a driven rod 30 feet away. The worker making contact with the front or rear of the truck encountered 5,304 to 5,601 volts and 5.8 to 6.0 amperes for voltage and current, respectively.

The truck was then grounded to a #4 copper pole ground. In this third test, the worker encountered a voltage of 221 to 225 volts and a current of 240 to 255 milliamperes when making contact with the front or rear of the truck. The low current was probably not seen by relays as a fault.

Finally, the truck was grounded directly to the line neutral. When the worker made contact with the front or rear of the vehicle, the voltage was 21 to 221 volts and the current was 200 to 230 milliamperes. Several large electrical flashes, with accompanying noise, occurred.

Personal Protective Grounding with Insulated Boom Devices

Because of the possibility of the elevated worker contacting a component that has some voltage present and a grounded contact point, such as a pole down wire,

Figure 10-10   Ground Worker Using a Conductive Mat

Figure 10-10. Ground workers around a truck must use a conductive mat to ensure their safety.

crossarm, or transformer case, it is essential that an equipotential zone be created around the elevated worker.

The use of separate grounds may be acceptable for devices with insulated booms, because the worker in the bucket is isolated from earth by the insulated boom.

See Figure 10-11. The connection to the conductor at the platform develops the equipotential zone for the workers aloft. The truck ground bleeds a capacitive-coupled current and maintains low voltage on the truck to lower the risk of step and touch hazards for the ground worker.

Thus, an insulated truck has a capacitive-coupled voltage to the upper boom's metal parts and to the truck body, a small arc between the worker and the line upon contact, and separate grounds that keep the charging current to a minimum. **See Figure 10-12.**

However, if the elbow of the boom, which is found below the insulated upper boom, can contact a line with voltage, the truck may become energized. Some trucks have a lower insulated boom insert to further protect ground workers. The use of a common ground would be appropriate if the truck body could become energized in this manner and no lower boom insert is present.

Figure 10-11	Using Separate Grounds with Insulated Booms

Figure 10-11. Master grounds have been installed on the line some distance from the workers. Because the workers are in an aerial lift with insulated boom sections, the use of separate grounds could provide adequate protection.

Figure 10-12 Insulated Boom Isolates Aloft Workers

Figure 10-12. *The bucket and insulated boom sections provide barriers to current flow between the workers and paths to ground through the truck chassis.*

Summary

A truck is often grounded through a driven ground rod, which gives a faulted line sufficient current to operate the line's protective equipment. Vehicles that may contact a grounded system should be connected to that system by means of a portable cable assembly. Ground cables on reels or looped on vehicles should not be coiled. Vehicles that a worker can contact simultaneously should be connected to a common ground. This includes metal boom trucks, where workers are at 0 volts before line contact is made; a common ground may or may not be required when using a truck with an insulated boom. However, driven and truck grounds protect the line, not the worker.

The worker protection methods that should be used when working around trucks are isolation (barricades), insulation, and equipotential zones, particularly through the use of portable mats. One method of protection is to establish an equipotential zone when working from an elevated platform. Workers at ground level must be protected from both step and touch voltage hazards.

Review Questions

1. All elbow type bucket trucks are constructed with insulated sections in both the upper and lower booms.

   a. True

   b. False

2. Two workers are in contact with a boom truck that is energized at full line voltage. One worker is immediately adjacent to a lowered outrigger and the other is at the front of the truck. The touch potential risk for the worker positioned at the front of the truck is __?__ that of the worker at the outrigger.

   a. equal to

   b. greater than

   c. less than

   d. similar to

3. When a grounded vehicle is in contact with a grounded conductor, no one should approach within __?__ feet of the vehicle.

   a. 5

   b. 10

   c. 15

   d. 20

4. When it is necessary for ground level workers to be near grounded equipment or vehicles, they can be protected with bonded conductive mats, insulated platforms, or __?__ .

   a. approved insulated footwear

   b. insulated tools

   c. rubber cover-up equipment

   d. voltage rated rubber gloves

5. Because a worker in a bucket with an insulated boom is isolated from the earth buy the boom, the use of a separate ground may be acceptable.

   a. True

   b. False

Underground Distribution Grounding

The hazards present during underground maintenance are similar to those encountered elsewhere in utility maintenance. The protection is limited to insulation or equipotential zones. Equipment is mounted at grade level or buried in earth. The workers are normally on earth or in a buried vault. As with truck grounding, many of the standard protective techniques and principles can be used in underground distribution work.

Objectives

» Explain the use of insulation as a protective technique in underground distribution applications.

» Describe the use of equipotential zones as a protective technique in underground distribution applications.

» Understand how the use of portable ground mats can help the worker develop equipotential zones when performing some midspan work tasks.

Chapter 11

Table of Contents

UNDERGROUND MAINTENANCE HAZARDS

The hazards present during underground maintenance are similar to those encountered elsewhere in utility maintenance, although some unique hazards may be encountered while working underground.

Particular Hazards of Underground Work Areas and Conditions

Underground cables are tubular capacitors. The center conductor is insulated from the outer semiconductive insulation shielding. It takes a long time for the charge to bleed off naturally. The cable must be discharged before it is contacted.

Underground work methods normally require initial contact with elbows, cables, and other components to be made with an insulated hot line tool, or hot stick. Once the cable has been deenergized and the elbows have been parked on grounded bushings, it is considered isolated and safe to proceed with the work.

Many accidents occur when an elbow is replaced on an energized bushing. In many cases, a worker moved an elbow from a safe parking bushing to an energized bushing while work was in progress. Accidents also have been reported from incorrect phase identification of buried cables when cutting midspan, removing

elbows by hand without insulated tools, and other worker errors.

Hazards of Midspan Splicing

Cutting buried cables midspan to add equipment, after grounding the conductor and neutral on both ends, still presents multiple problems. After opening a hole and verifying that the cable has been deenergized, the cable can be cut with insulated tools. The conductor is grounded at the ends by parking the elbows on grounded stand-off bushings. A temporary jumper must be connected to the concentric neutrals across the cut cable ends. A portable conductive mat is bonded to the cable neutral. **See Figure 11-1.** A hot stick is used to isolate elbows and install jumpers and a safety mat.

The underground worker is in an equipotential zone while on the mat. The zone is required because the cut cable may become accidentally energized from either end and the worker is in contact with both conductor and earth. The grounded end provides the line trip current. A serious hazard exists until these connections are in place and the worker is safely on the mat. Special attention must be paid to ensure that the cable is not energized during this connection time, either from worker error or from induction.

UNDERGROUND MAINTENANCE PROTECTION METHODS

Underground protection is limited to insulation or equipotential zones because barricades would get in the way. However, even insulation and equipotential zones are sometimes difficult to implement because of work areas and conditions. Underground workers must remember that skipping a step may put them in peril.

Workers must identify circuits clearly before beginning underground work and test for the presence of voltage on the circuit being maintained. It is important that underground workers always ensure the circuit is "dead" by ensuring the spiker is reliable and maintain a safe distance while spiking. Spiking involves

Figure 11-1. Midspan Cable Splicing

Figure 11-1. The conductor is grounded by parking elbows on grounded stand-off bushings. At the splice point, the cable jacket is removed and a temporary grounding jumper is connected across the open cable ends. Splicing is done from a conductive mat bonded to the cable neutral.

Figure 11-2 Spiking

Figure 11-2. A circuit must be deenergized before spiking work is undertaken.

mechanically or hydraulically driving a grounded pin into an insulated power cable to ensure it is electrically isolated before the insulation is opened. **See Figure 11-2.** Underground workers also must isolate the circuit by placing each end on a grounded parking bushing using a "shotgun" hot stick and make sure the circuit is grounded on both ends.

Around pad-mounted switches or transformers the use of portable ground mats establishes an equipotential zone and protects workers who remain on the mats. An additional ground connection for the fault current must be present. The mat is not designed to be the trip current path.

When splicing damaged buried cable midspan, the equipotential zone, conductor, and neutral connections can be established using rubber gloves or insulated tools. At some point in the splicing operation, it becomes necessary to remove these connections. The worker who then contacts the conductor for splicing becomes a direct path to earth. The portable ground mat no longer offers protection because the worker is a path to ground whether on or off of a mat. The hazards that are present are hand-to-hand contact between conductor ends being spliced or hand-through-body contact to earth. This is an especially hazardous period.

UNDERGROUND MAINTENANCE PROTECTION EQUIPMENT

A portable equipotential mat is necessary for underground maintenance protection. In addition to the portable mat, an underground distribution ground set is a key piece of protective equipment for workers maintaining an underground system. The set comes in single- and 3-phase forms.

Portable Equipotential Mat

A portable equipotential mat provides an equipotential zone for the underground worker and protects against step and touch potential. This portable ground grid maintains a low-voltage drop across the worker during underground work. **See Figure 11-3.**

The mat does not provide protection during underground splicing, when the bonding jumper and mat are removed.

Figure 11-3 Portable Conductive Mat

Figure 11-3. A portable conductive mat limits hazardous voltage drop across the underground worker caused by the voltage gradient at the underground worksite.

Single-Phase Underground Distribution Ground Set

A single-phase underground distribution ground set is rated for 10 kiloamperes at 10 cycles. **See Figure 11-4.**

3-Phase Underground Distribution Ground Set

The 3-phase underground distribution set provides high visibility of the ground elbow. The elbow mounts directly to a ground bushing or feed-through bushing. **See Figure 11-5.**

UNDERGROUND MAINTENANCE VAULT TESTS

Tests have been conducted with workers inside reinforced concrete vaults, buried to grade level. When connections were made bonding the conductor, the neutral, and the vault together, the conductive vault formed an equipotential zone around the worker. When only the conductor and neutral were bonded together, the worker still had some protection when the neutral was continuous to the source. In that case, the neutral was a low-resistance return

Figure 11-4	Single-Phase Grounded Parking Bushing

Figure 11-4. An underground cable may be grounded by connecting the elbow termination to a temporary mounted grounded bushing.

Figure 11-5	Three-Phase Underground Distribution Ground Set

Figure 11-5. A 3-phase distribution set is one option for underground work.

path in parallel with the worker and earth path. However, when the neutral was not continuous, the worker was fatally energized because the current return path was through the worker and earth. **See Figure 11-6.**

Protective grounds bonding the conductor to the neutral and to the vault in adjacent vaults offer some worker protection when the conductors and neutral are both present and continuous. In that case, the conductor, neutral, and bonding jumpers in parallel with the worker form an equipotential zone. However, the resistance of these conductors and connections may be sufficiently high to exceed the specified voltage across a worker. The resulting circuit should be analyzed before using this method. It would not be a safe practice to rely upon the unconfirmed presence of a continuous neutral to the source. Precautions should be taken at the worksite to ensure worker protection.

Underground Maintenance Test Series

For the test series, the vaults were 300 feet apart and flush to earth, with an aluminum 2/0 American Wire Gauge (AWG) ring ground inside the vault and underground 2/0 AWG cable in polyvinyl chloride conduit. **See Figure 11-7.** There was a remote ground, a single

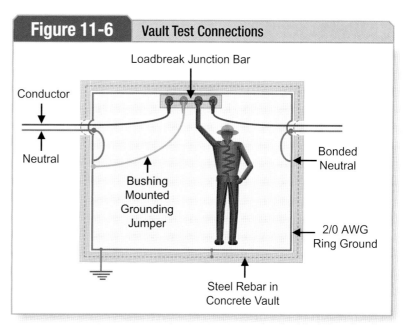

Figure 11-6. *The primary conductor is 2/0 AWG cable terminated with elbows on a loadbreak junction bar. The line and load side neutral are bonded to the 2/0 AWG vault ring ground. Vault tests revealed that a continuous neutral was essential to worker safety while underground.*

ground in the source side vault, and continuous and noncontinuous source neutrals. Workers were inside of the steel-reinforced concrete vaults, contacting various parts inside the vault. Less than 6.5 volts were across each worker in these tests.

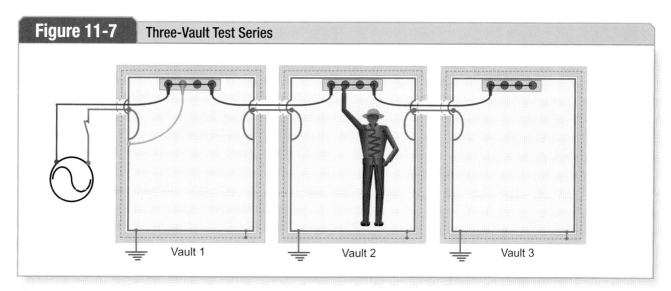

Figure 11-7. *Three vaults spaced 300 feet apart were used in the underground maintenance test series.*

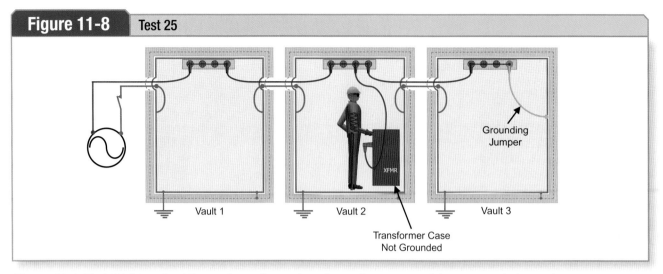

Figure 11-8. *Test 25 determined the worker voltage when the worker contacted the ungrounded transformer case.*

Maintenance Test 25

In test 25, the worker was in contact with the transformer case. The neutral was energized by a jumper between the neutral and the conductor. The transformer case was energized by a normal neutral-to-case connection. In this test, worker voltage was 748 volts. Without grounding in the working vault, the worker becomes another path to the source. **See Figure 11-8.**

Maintenance Test 72

In test 72, the worker voltage was 416 volts. Loss of a continuous neutral to source increased worker voltage. **See Figure 11-9.**

Maintenance Test 74

Test 74 had the same conditions as test 72 except that the neutral to source was continuous. The conductor was grounded to the concentric neutral. This

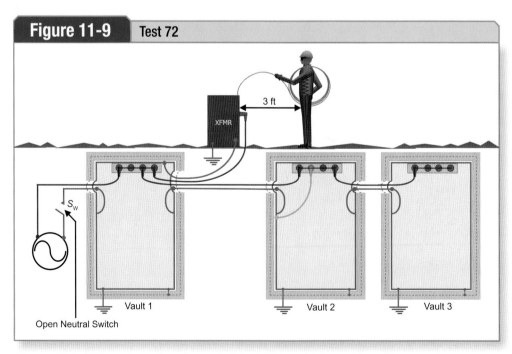

Figure 11-9. *Without a continuous neutral, test 72 saw high worker voltage.*

concentric neutral was a low-resistance path in parallel with but not visible to the worker. The worker voltage was 1.5 volts, but the worker was saved by luck. **See Figure 11-10.**

Maintenance Test with Protective Mat

A further maintenance test was conducted with a protective mat in place.

The voltage across the worker was held to only 1.5 volts. **See Figure 11-11.** Clearly, this mat should be part of all protection schemes to avoid unknown and unseen hazards.

Thus, this test series found that, if a conductor is ungrounded in a working vault and the vault ring ground is not connected to neutral, then the worker is isolated and unprotected.

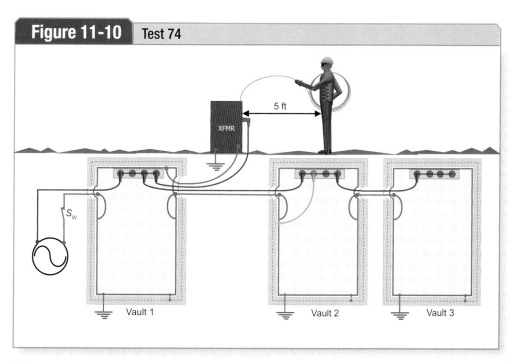

Figure 11-10. *A continuous neutral resulted in a lower worker voltage in test 74 compared to test 72, but its presence was not confirmed and thus not ensured.*

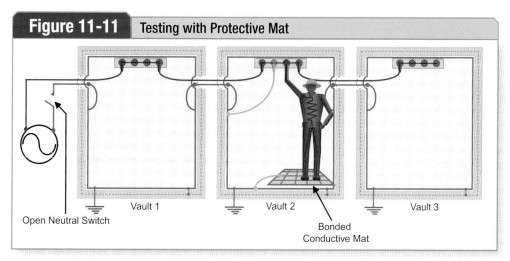

Figure 11-11. *The best results in the underground maintenance test series were found when a conductive protective mat was placed beneath the worker.*

Summary

Underground protection methods are the same as the standard methods of isolation, insulation, and equipotential zone creation. However, isolation is often impossible, given the working conditions. Even insulation and equipotential zones can be difficult to incorporate into underground projects, so workers must take extra care in setting up and removing their equipment and fulfilling their job tasks.

Portable ground mats must be used to develop equipotential zones around surface-mounted equipment, and underground distribution ground sets are required for workers maintaining an underground system. Vault work requires particular care: The presence of an unconfirmed neutral is not reliable protection when working in a vault. All other necessary safety precautions must be taken before beginning underground work.

Many protective issues arise when cutting buried cables midspan to add equipment, even after grounding the conductor and neutral on both ends. Portable ground mats must be used to develop equipotential zones when performing some underground midspan work to provide protection from voltage differences. However, protective grounding cannot be provided during the final steps of an underground midspan splice. When neutral connections must be removed to complete the process, the worker who comes into contact with the conductor becomes a path to ground—whether on or off of a mat.

Review Questions

1. **Underground cables must be discharged before contacting because they are a type of tubular   ? .**
    a.   capacitor
    b.   inductor
    c.   reactor
    d.   transformer

2. **When making midspan repairs on buried cables, reported accidents have been caused by   ? .**
    a.   discharging with hot line tools
    b.   failure to park elbows on insulated standoff bushings
    c.   incorrect phase identification
    d.   spiking isolated cables

3. **While performing underground equipment maintenance, a person is equipotential zone protected while working   ? .**
    a.   on isolated conductors
    b.   from a portable conductive mat
    c.   when standing on the earth near a ground rod
    d.   with rated rubber gloves

4. **Underground vault tests revealed that a   ?   was essential to worker safety.**
    a.   continuous neutral
    b.   cluster bar with jumper
    c.   ring ground
    d.   steel rebar cage

5. **When making a midspan cable splice, an equipotential zone using a grounded mat will protect the worker throughout the complete splicing process.**
    a.   True
    b.   False

Protective Grounding in Substations

Substations present hazards involving voltage and current, step and touch potentials, and accidental reenergizing of the equipment. The same protective methods used in most situations may be used in substations. However, maintenance is more problematic in substations because of the types, quantity, and proximity of equipment. Fault currents are also typically greater in substations than on remote lines. Work on substations requires consideration of the importance of providing protection against electrical arc blasts and flashes.

Objectives

» Describe protective grounding techniques that can be used in substation applications.

» Calculate the acceptable voltage and current levels for exposed workers in substations.

» Understand the importance of keeping personal protective grounds as close to the worker as possible in substation applications.

Chapter 12

Table of Contents

HAZARDS OF SUBSTATION MAINTENANCE

Substations present all of the hazards of overhead grounding, including induced voltage and current and accidental reenergizing of the equipment. Step and touch potential hazards may be present, but these normally occur at a reduced level in substations, where the substation grid helps minimize them. **See Figure 12-1.**

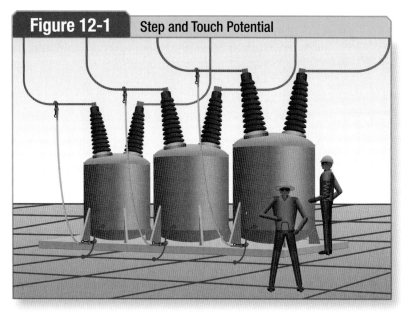

Figure 12-1 | **Step and Touch Potential**

Figure 12-1. During fault current flow, the entire substation grid surface rises to nearly the same voltage as the line, reducing step and touch potential risks. In substations, these hazards are less likely compared to other work sites.

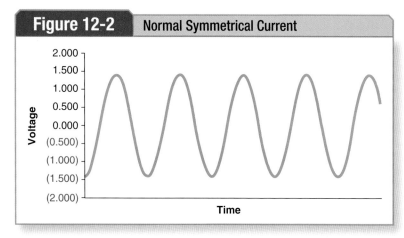

Figure 12-2 | **Normal Symmetrical Current**

Figure 12-2. With a normal symmetrical current, the voltage rises and falls the same amount as it cycles over time.

Maintenance is a problem in substations because of the great variety of equipment installed, the methods of performing maintenance on these items, and the normal presence of energized buses and conductors nearby. Because of the quantity of the equipment found in substations, as well as its size and weight, positioning is frequently an issue. Both induced voltage and induced current present hazards that arise from the proximity of energized items. Backfeed is another issue that occurs when power flows are reversed. Finally, in substations, strong fault currents and the presence of highly inductive items cause an asymmetrical current during a fault.

Size and Weight of Required Grounding Equipment

Much greater fault currents are typical for a substation compared with the fault currents found on a remote line. The larger currents require larger personal protective grounding equipment to safely carry them. The weight and positioning of these grounds may become an issue.

The use of multiple grounding points, such as substation grounding switches and personal protective grounds, forms a loop, allowing induced current to flow. The low-resistance substation grid completes the loop. This current may be quite large because of the proximity of energized equipment or buses. However, the use of multiple grounding connections to the substation grid tends to divide the current among multiple paths and thus lower the current at the worksite.

Asymmetrical Currents

A normal current is symmetrical about the zero axis. **See Figure 12-2.**

In contrast, an asymmetrical current is a current that, at the beginning of flow, becomes significantly offset from the zero axis of a normal symmetrical current. The asymmetrical current and its components look quite different from those of a normal symmetrical current. **See Figure 12-3.**

The direct current (DC) voltage of an asymmetrical current can be shown over time. **See Figure 12-4.**

X/R Ratios

The cause of the asymmetrical current is the large amount of inductance present from the reactors and transformers in comparison to the small amount of resistance present in the buses. The greater the inductance-to-resistance ratio, the more pronounced the initial offset. This is also called the *X/R* ratio, or the ratio of reactance (X) to resistance (R), where the reactance is usually caused by inductance (X_L). The X_L/R ratio must be considered when working in substations.

X_L/R CONSIDERATIONS

Sources of inductive reactance are power transformers, neutral reactors, and instrument transformers (that is, potential and current transformers). All are common items in substations and switchyards.

Increases in Inductive Reactance and Asymmetrical Current

Increases in inductive reactance cause an increase in the asymmetrical current. It can have an extremely high first loop peak current value. **See Figure 12-5.**

The peak current of the first loop may be nearly 2.5 times the normal root-mean-square (rms) current value at a ratio of 30:1. The mechanical force associated with current flow varies as the square of the current.

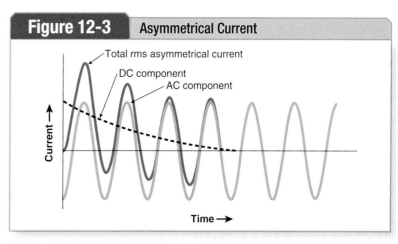

Figure 12-3. *Over time, an asymmetrical current drops from its high point and becomes inconsistent.*

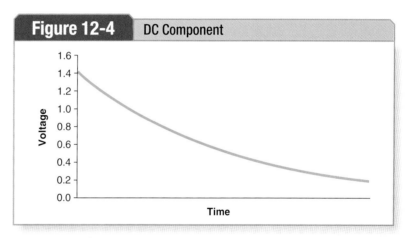

Figure 12-4. *Over time, the direct current component of an asymmetrical current decreases.*

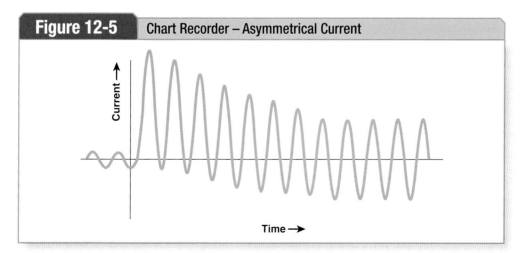

Figure 12-5. *As seen on a chart recorder, an increase occurs in the peak current of the first loop of the asymmetrical current, and the entire asymmetrical current is offset from the axis representing time.*

Results of High Currents in Substations

High currents available in substations result in huge forces on grounding items. The resulting mechanical force may be up to eight times the normal level at a maximum ratio. Normal bus current $(1.414 \times I_{rms})$ asymmetry doubles the peak, and squaring the bus current $(2.828 \times I_{rms}^2)$ asymmetry gives up to eight times the force.

Potential Equipment Failure

Aluminum welded grounding connection points often break off from the bus under these normal and squared forces, removing protection provided by the grounds. Improperly selected clamps may break, or ferrules may pull out of the clamps under eight times the normal force. Special bus connections should be provided that can withstand these forces, yet carry the current.

Additional heating occurs because of the offset asymmetrical current, further softening the copper and allowing a mechanical failure that occurs just before melting. **See Figure 12-6.**

Risks to Worker

The voltage drop across a protective grounding cable, when carrying maximum anticipated fault current, must be low enough to prevent hazardous current flow through the worker's body. The values of the voltage drop must not exceed 100 volts for 15-hertz (250-millisecond) substation clearing. **See Figure 12-7.**

Low-resistance protective ground cables limit the voltage drop at the worksite to acceptable levels. Therefore, it is imperative that the protective ground cables be designed and assembled to handle the maximum acceptable levels of the anticipated fault current. Transmission line and substation bus fault currents must be calculated from the electrical parameters of the power system to identify the size and number of protective ground cables required.

Typically, each utility field office develops an annual listing of the maximum anticipated fault currents for each of its transmission lines and substation buses. If parallel grounds are to be used, it also lists the proper size and number of protective grounding cables anticipated in each facility. Circuits carrying significant induced currents should include their maximum anticipated continuous current. This listing must be reviewed and updated annually to ensure proper sizing of protective grounding cables. A copy of this data is typically submitted each year to the respective crews working at each facility, as well as to the technical support and safety divisions of the utility.

Anything that interrupts the protective parallel path puts the substation worker at risk. When working between grounds, outside connections must not be between the grounds. For personal safety, the substation worker must not depend on any device that can transform or develop a voltage drop.

Figure 12-6	ASTM Standard F855

High Asymmetrical Test Requirements

Grade	Size	Rating Rated Current (kA)	X/R = 30 1st Cycle Current Peak (kA) X 2.69	Last Cycle Current Peak (kA)	Test Duration (cycles)
1H	No. 2	15	41	23	15
2H	1/0	25	65	37	15
3H	2/0	31	84	46	15
4H	3/0	39	105	58	15
5H	4/0	47	126	70	15
6H	250 MCM	55	148	82	15
7H	350 MCM	68	183	101	15

Note 1—The above current values are based on electromechanical test values.
Note 2—Assemblies that have been subjected to these shall not be reused.
Note 3—For use with currents exceeding 20% asymmetry factor.
Note 4—See X4.7.2 for additional information.
Note 5—Alternate testing circuits are available for laboratories that cannot achieve the above requirements. See Appendix X4 for details.

Figure 12-6. Larger available currents in substations require greater current-carrying capabilities for copper grounding cables.

Table 2 of ASTM F855 Specifications for Temporary Protective Grounds to Be Used on De-energized Electric Power Lines and Equipment re-printed with permission from ASTM International. Copyright ASTM International, 100 Barr Harbor Drive, West Conshohocken, PA 19428. All Rights Reserved. Full standard available at www.astm.org.

PROTECTIVE GROUNDING TECHNIQUES IN SUBSTATIONS

In substations, the same protective methods may be used as in overhead grounding: isolation, insulation, and equipotential zones.

While substation workers are within the minimum approach distance of deenergized, or electrically isolated, current-carrying components, such as conductors and bushing terminals, personal protective grounds should be in place. This includes grounds on instrument transformers, coupling capacitors, surge arresters, and similar station equipment, as well as grounds on power circuit breakers and power transformers while workers are inside the equipment tanks or on top of equipment. The minimum approach distances given in Chapter 8 also apply to substations.

Work on deenergized substation equipment and circuits should be performed with protective ground cables placed at the worksite. **See Figure 12-8.** The grounding cables should be visible from the worksite. Workers should bond grounding cables to a structure member, common copper equipment, or the structure ground lead, which is in turn bonded to the station ground mat and then to each bushing lead of the respective equipment.

On all electrical apparatus, the non–current-carrying parts (such as transformer cases, circuit breaker tanks, oil storage tanks, rails, piping, screens, metal fences, switch platforms, and guards) are permanently grounded by a copper conductor to the station ground mat. In substation grounding, a copper bar is sometimes used to connect 3-phase cables; a fourth cable is then connected to a riser from the station ground mat. Using multiple grounds to the grid reduces the fault current through each connection. Single-phase grounding is not allowed in substations.

These grounds are physically inspected periodically (such as during substation inspections) to ensure a good electrical and mechanical bond. They are not

Figure 12-7	Clearing Times

System Voltage (in kilovolts)	Primary Clearing (in cycles)
765/500/345	2–8
230/138/115	3–8
69	4–40
46/34	4–60
25/12/4	5–120

Figure 12-7. Typical clearing times are based on the system voltage in substations.

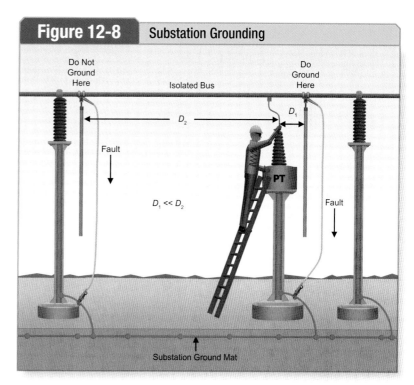

Figure 12-8. Substation grounding requires specific distances (D) between equipment and circuits. Distance D$_1$ should be kept as small as is reasonable.

removed while the equipment is in service. Equipment requiring multiple grounds has each ground visually inspected.

Work on high-voltage disconnect switches and bus conductors should be performed with protective grounding cables installed at the worksite. The grounding cables should be visible from the worksite. No switch is used to maintain continuity between the protective grounds and the worksite.

Work on high-voltage cables is done with protective grounds installed at each end of the cable on high-voltage insulated electrical terminals that transition from the overhead to the underground cable. If the cable to be opened lies in a network of cables, or if there is doubt as to whether the cable is deenergized, the cable is spiked (using an approved mechanical or hydraulic tool) with a grounded pin before it is opened. When a cable is to be opened or spliced, grounds are installed at the worksite if such grounding is feasible. Such grounds should remain in place until the conductor is joined, after which the grounds may be removed for taping or reinsulating the splice.

Grounding transformers are not worked on unless they have been deenergized and properly grounded. Phase reactors are electrically isolated from all energized sources and grounded.

During testing, high voltages for ground instrument transformers may be generated. After fully charged capacitor banks (series and shunt) have been deenergized, most capacitors are discharged by waiting at least five minutes to permit the capacitors to drain through the internal discharge resistor. The capacitor bank grounding switch, if available, is closed, and protective grounds are applied. An additional five minutes is allowed after the ground switch is closed before the clearance is issued that permits protective grounds to be installed. Short the individual capacitors from terminal to terminal and from terminal to case by approved means. If possible, substation workers should wait several hours after a capacitor failure before shunting, grounding, and handling bulged units to allow cooling and relieving of internal pressure. The time required for these maneuvers is explicitly expressed in switching orders involving capacitor banks.

Workers ground parked vehicles that are involved in substation maintenance activities to the station ground mat, using a grounding cable or cables of adequate size, if the vehicle is subject to coming within the minimum approach distances. During oil-handling operations on oil-filled equipment (such as transformers, regulators, and circuit breakers), the following precautions should be observed:

1. Apparatus tanks, shielded hoses, pumping or filtering equipment, drums, tank cars, trucks, and portable storage tanks are solidly bonded to the substation ground mat. Workers connect the vehicle ground end first and disconnect it last to prevent possible arcs near the vehicle.
2. Exposed conductors (such as transformer or circuit breaker bushings, as well as coil ends of a transformer with the bushing physically removed) are connected to the same grounding system.

When returning to work on a partially completed oil-filtering job after shutdown for any reason, all switching, bonding, and grounding should be checked before the workers resume the operation.

Protective grounds should be in place on transformers and oil circuit breakers before the oil is drained from the tanks or the tanks are opened. Bushing leads may be disconnected from bushing terminals as necessary to permit equipment testing (power factor test or oscillographic contact tests) that require the equipment terminals to be ungrounded. The bushing leads may be temporarily ungrounded (using a hot stick) to permit these tests. The ground is reestablished as soon as the test is completed. Grounding instructions for the test equipment are in accordance with the manufacturer's recommendations.

In all instances, the personal protective ground should be kept as close to the worker as possible to minimize parallel resistance.

INSTITUTE OF ELECTRICAL AND ELECTRONICS ENGINEERS STANDARD RECOMMENDATIONS

Substation work methods may be designed around Institute of Electrical and Electronics Engineers (IEEE) Standard 1246. The same principles as those defined for overhead maintenance are used in the IEEE standard, but substation applications and examples are given. For example, IEEE recommendations are to discharge all capacitors before contact and to ground instrument transformers during testing because high voltage may be developed by the transformer action. A key recommendation in the IEEE standard is to keep the personal protective ground that is connected from the bus or the equipment to the grid as close to the worksite as possible.

Consider an example that uses the low-resistance substation grid as the path that completes the induced current loops. **See Figure 12-9.**

The assumptions are as follows:

$$E = 345 \text{ kV}$$
$$I_F = 30,000 \text{ A}$$
$$R = 2 \ \Omega$$

where E is the 3-phase voltage, I_F is the available fault current, and R is the conductive lift resistance. In addition, the example assumes an aluminum bus with a cross-section area of 2,500 thousand circular mils (with resistance of 0.007 ohm for every 1,000 feet) and grid conductors equal to 250 thousand circular mils (with resistance of 0.028 ohm for every 400 feet). Two 40-foot jumpers (with resistance of 0.0054 ohm) are also used, one on each side of the worksite. The spacing between the first jumper and the worker's point of contact is 400 feet. The same spacing is used in the opposite direction between the worker's point of contact and the second jumper. The worker is standing on the platform of an uninsulated man lift with a resistance of two ohms.

The following first current was found at the substation worksite before the first contact:

$$I_1 = 30,000 \times \left[\frac{(0.0028 + 0.0028 + 0.0054 + 0.028 + 0.028)}{(0.0028 + 0.0028 + 0.0054 + 0.028 + 0.028 + 0.0054)} \right]$$

$$= 30,000 \times \left(\frac{0.067}{0.0724} \right)$$

$$= 27,763 \text{ A}$$

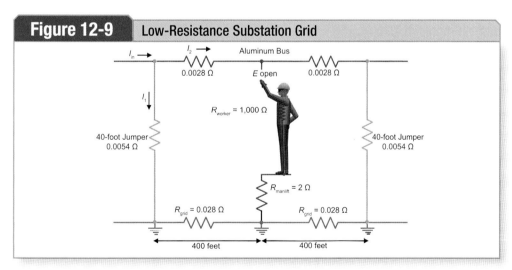

Figure 12-9 Low-Resistance Substation Grid

Figure 12-9. The low-resistance substation grid is part of the completed induced current. Bracket grounds are connected to the substation ground grid. Using the given voltage, resistances, and fault current values, the open circuit voltage across the overhead bus and the worker is approximately 81 volts.

From this first current of 27,763 amperes, remaining currents and voltages can be determined as follows:

$$I_2 = 30{,}000 - 27{,}763 = 2{,}238 \text{ A}$$
$$E_1 = 27{,}763 \times 0.0054 = 150 \text{ V}$$
$$E_2 = 2{,}238 \times 0.0028 = 6.27 \text{ V}$$

Here, V_1 is the voltage developed by I_1 across the 0.0054-ohm resistor, and V_2 is the voltage dropped by I_2 across each 0.0028-ohm bus/grid section. In addition, voltage was found across the 0.0054-ohm jumper ($2{,}238 \times 0.0054 = 12.1$ volts) and across the 0.028-ohm grid points ($2{,}238 \times 0.028 = 62.7$ volts). Therefore, voltage across the open gap, before contact, was as follows:

$$E = 6.27 + 12.1 + 62.7 = 81.07 \text{ V}$$

After making contact, the current division changes. **See Figure 12-10.**

$$R_{EQ} = (1{,}000 + 2) \times \left[\frac{(0.0028 + 0.0054 + 0.028)}{(1{,}000 + 2 + 0.0028 + 0.0054 + 0.028)} \right]$$
$$= 1{,}002 \times \left(\frac{0.0362}{1{,}002.0362} \right)$$
$$= 0.036 \ \Omega$$
$$I_1 = 30{,}000 \times \left[\frac{(0.0028 + 0.036 + 0.028)}{(0.0028 + 0.036 + 0.028 + 0.005)} \right]$$
$$= 30{,}000 \times \left(\frac{0.0668}{0.0718} \right)$$
$$= 27{,}911 \text{ A}$$
$$I_2 = 30{,}000 - 27{,}911 = 2{,}089 \text{ A}$$

Here, R_{EQ} is the value of a single imaginary resistor for the right parallel part of the circuit, which could be substituted for the entire parallel group of resistors without changing the electrical properties of the circuit.

The division of currents after making contact can then be used to determine the worker current (I_W) and worker voltage (E_W) as follows:

$$I_W = 2{,}089 \times \left[\frac{(0.0028 + 0.0054 + 0.028)}{(1{,}000 + 2 + 0.0028 + 0.0054 + 0.028)} \right]$$
$$= 2{,}089 \times \left(\frac{0.0362}{1{,}002.0362} \right)$$
$$= 0.075 \text{ A}$$
$$E_W = 0.075 \times 1{,}000 = 75 \text{ V}$$

The 75 volts with 75 milliamperes provides borderline safety. Compared to the bracket grounds at a remote maintenance or construction site, working over (and connected to) the substation yard grid is a huge improvement. The difference is the values of earth's resistance versus the grid resistance.

SUBSTATION EQUIPMENT

The same equipment is found overhead and in a substation: clamps, ferrules, and cables.

One specialized tool is particularly useful in substation work: an all-angle ground clamp. This clamp installs at a wider range of angles than other clamps. This range is facilitated by its maximum opening of 2.88 inches. Rated grade 5 (43 kiloamperes at 15 cycles), the clamp comes with pressure- or threaded-type terminals. It can have an eye screw or be set up for mounting on a stick. **See Figure 12-11.**

Figure 12-10 | Current Division Changes

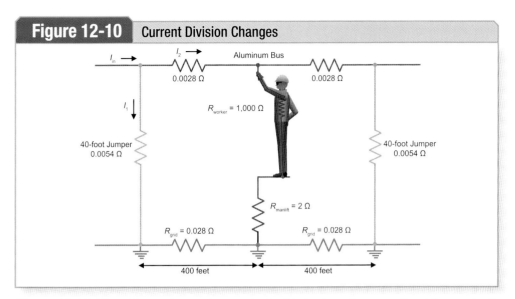

Figure 12-10. When the worker makes contact with the bus, the currents at the work site change. The worker will have a 75-volt potential difference from hand to feet. A body current of 75 milliamps flows between worker contact points. In substation work, keep personal protective grounds as close to the worker as possible.

Figure 12-11 | All-Angle Ground Clamp

Figure 12-11. An all-angle ground clamp is a particularly useful tool for substation work.

Summary

Substations are highly hazardous worksites because extreme mechanical forces may be available. The large variety of installed substation items also increases the need for thoughtful grounding procedures. The strong fault currents and highly inductive items found in a substation can cause an asymmetrical current during a fault. This means that higher-rated equipment is needed in substations compared with overhead worksites. Therefore, grounding equipment specifications must be verified to ensure they meet substation requirements. To ensure the highest levels of protection, multiple ground points should be used within a substation. In addition, personal protective grounds should be as close to the worker as possible for substation jobs.

Review Questions

1. Step and touch potentials are minimized by the __?__ at substation worksites.
    a. grid
    b. grounded perimeter fence
    c. increased insulation levels
    d. tall steel bus supports

2. The cause of asymmetrical current in substations is the large amount of inductance present from reactors and transformers in comparison to the __?__.
    a. bus to earth capacitive coupling
    b. high fault current levels
    c. low resistance of the ground grid
    d. small amount of resistance present in the buses

3. During a substation fault current event, the direct current component of an asymmetrical current will __?__ over time.
    a. decrease
    b. increase
    c. pulse at the 60 cycle rate
    d. remain constant

4. The high currents available in substations result in mechanical forces up to __?__ times the normal level at a maximum ratio.
    a. four
    b. eight
    c. twelve
    d. sixteen

5. In substations, the personal protective ground should be __?__.
    a. at least 10 feet away from the worker
    b. as close to the worker as possible
    c. within sight of the worker
    d. unrestrained

Protective Grounding During Construction

Grounding during construction presents hazards that are specific but not unique from those of standard grounding. The hazards of accidental energizing, step and touch potential, and induced voltage remain. Several specialized types of equipment have been developed to maintain the integrity of the grounding scheme during the construction process. There are several special grounding considerations to keep in mind when designing protective grounding schemes during construction.

Objectives

» Explain the requirements for vehicles and placement of workers during construction.

» Describe the basic protective techniques that provide worker protection during construction.

» Understand the special equipment needs when installing grounding schemes during construction.

Chapter 13

Table of Contents

CONSTRUCTION SITE HAZARDS

Maintaining a safe work area is more difficult during construction for several reasons:
- More workers are present and need to be watched, controlled, and protected.
- More vehicles increase the places that can become hazard sites.
- Work often occurs near energized lines.

Figure 13-1. *The force of the compression spring keeps the rollers of this running ground in firm contact with the conductor or wire rope pulling line.*

The increased activity makes it easy to concentrate on the work and overlook a potential hazard or accident about to happen.

Still, the hazards facing construction site workers are not unique. They remain possible fault currents and accidental energizing, step and touch potentials, and induced voltages and currents.

Induction from energized lines may induce voltage in the lines under construction and in the construction equipment.

CONSTRUCTION SITE PROTECTION METHODS

An effective protection system at a construction site must do the following:
- Provide an equipotential zone or zones or a low-impedance path to earth
- Withstand fault and surge currents
- Be mechanically rugged (reliable)

The protections available for construction sites are insulation, isolation (barricades), and an established equipotential zone.

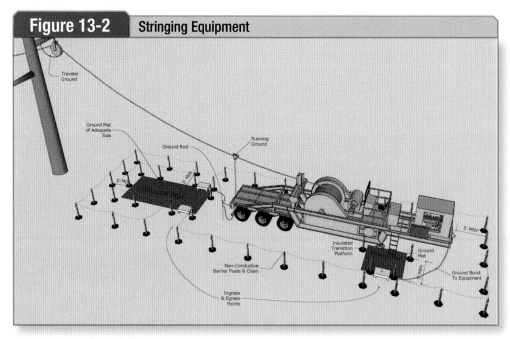

Figure 13-2. *Stringing equipment is common on worksites that involve new construction.*
Courtesy of Wilson Construction Co.

CONSTRUCTION WORKER PROTECTION METHODS

Although construction sites benefit from standard worker protection methods, such as barricades, ground mats, and vehicle and equipment grounding, a specific grounding method is primarily used to provide protection for personnel during construction or reconstruction operations. A running ground, also referred to as rolling ground, is a portable device designed to connect a moving conductor or wire rope to an electrical ground. The device is sometimes called a ground roller or moving roller. **See Figure 13-1.**

Rolling ground devices are normally placed on the conductor or wire rope adjacent to the pulling and tensioning equipment located at either end of a wire pull.

With new construction or when installing temporary lines, stringing equipment — such as reel stands, trailers, pullers, and tensioners — is used. **See Figure 13-2.**

The stringing equipment is grounded, and the pieces of equipment are bonded

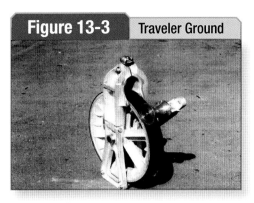

Figure 13-3 | Traveler Ground

Figure 13-3. Grounding stringing blocks or traveler grounds connect the electrical ground to a wire rope or moving conductor.

to one another and to each conductor, overhead ground wire, or conductive pulling line. Stringing blocks with electrically conductive neoprene linings are not used to replace the grounding requirements of grounding stringing blocks. **See Figure 13-3.**

A running ground is installed on each conductor, overhead ground wire, or conductive pulling line between the tensioning equipment and the first structure. **See Figure 13-4.**

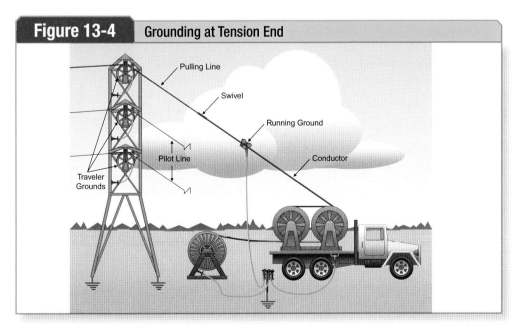

Figure 13-4 | Grounding at Tension End

Pulling Line

Swivel

Running Ground

Pilot Line

Conductor

Traveler Grounds

Figure 13-4. Jumpers connect the traveler grounds to the tower body. A running ground is placed between the conductor and ground rod. The conductor reel, truck chassis, and running ground are all connected to a common ground point..

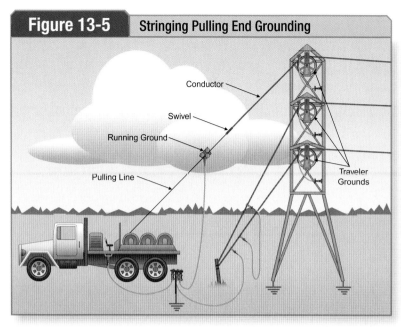

Figure 13-5 | **Stringing Pulling End Grounding**

Figure 13-5. At the pulling end of a stringing operation, a running ground is required if the pulling line is a wire rope.

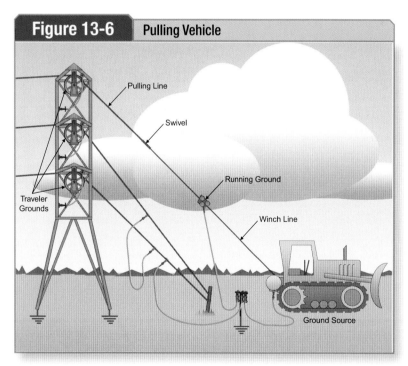

Figure 13-6 | **Pulling Vehicle**

Figure 13-6. A vehicle winch can be used to pull conductors to pre-sag tension. Note: Pulling vehicles using rubber tires require that the vehicle and the running ground be grounded.

During stringing operations, each bare conductor, subconductor, and overhead ground wire is also grounded at the first structure adjacent to the pulling setup. **See Figure 13-5.**

Metal tracked vehicles used for pulling need not be grounded. **See Figure 13-6.**

Often, the weak point in running and rolling grounds is the interface between the cable wheel and the grounding cable attachment point. The cable is often on the axle of the wheel. The wheel is electrically connected to the cable through a slip joint, allowing the wheel to turn. Thus, it is important to test rolling grounds before using them.

When performing work from the structures, clipping crews and all others working on conductors, subconductors, and overhead ground wires are protected by individual grounds installed on the phase being worked. When work is performed in the vicinity of insulated overhead ground wires, the specified working clearance for a 15-kilovolt circuit—0.66 meters (2 feet 2 inches)—must be maintained; otherwise, protective grounds must be applied.

Noninsulated overhead ground wires are electrically bonded to the structure grounding system before making contact with the overhead ground wire with the following exceptions:

- When momentary contact is made (such as when hanging hand lines)
- When personal protective grounds are not in place (such as during climbing inspections)

The overhead ground wire is always bonded to the structure ground by a personal protective ground cable when any part of the overhead ground wire connecting hardware is to be disconnected.

When installing grounds at a construction site, install and remove grounding equipment with an insulated hot line tool, and always connect the ground end first. **See Figure 13-7.**

If it is necessary to return to a structure during the stringing operation to complete structure or hardware installation, all conductors, subconductors, and over-head ground wires are grounded to the structure; otherwise, each ungrounded component is treated as energized. Use additional traveling grounds when paralleling energized lines. Never allow a worker to be in parallel with grounding equipment on the construction site. **See Figure 13-8.**

Grounds should be left in place until all work is completed. Grounds may be removed as soon as the work is completed, provided that the line is not left as an open circuit at the structure at which work is being completed.

When removing grounding equipment from a construction site, the following precautions must be taken:

- Always remove the connection from the normally ungrounded item first.
- Remove the connection from the grounded source last.
- Do not coil ground cables.
- Restrain cables to minimize whipping.

Accidents have been reported when, while pulling in a lower circuit, contact is made with an upper, or overbuild circuit.

The line being strung or removed should be grounded on both sides of the crossing (crossover or crossunder); if it is not, the line being strung or removed is considered to be and worked as though energized. Some utilities have specific procedures in place for their transmission lines. For example, when crossing a Western Area Power Administration transmission line, a clearance or hot line order must be obtained on the line in accordance with Western's Power System Switching Procedure. On other utility transmission or distribution lines, where practical, the automatic reclosing feature of the circuit-interrupting device, on the line being crossed, is made inoperative. If the automatic reclosing feature of the other facility's transmission or distribution line cannot be rendered inoperative, the line being pulled is considered to be energized. Traveling grounds are replaced with ground

Figure 13-7   Hot Stick

Figure 13-7. On construction sites, a hot stick should always be used when installing and removing grounding equipment.

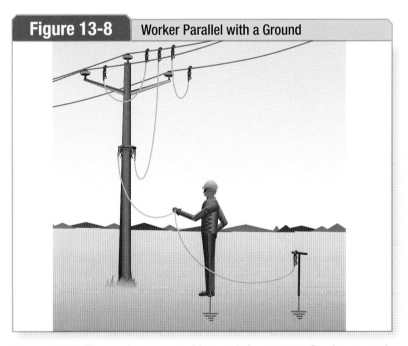

Figure 13-8   Worker Parallel with a Ground

Figure 13-8. The worker can provide a path for currents flowing to earth. Contact with cables or other grounded equipment is dangerous and must be avoided.

Figure 13-9 Barricades

Figure 13-9. Barricades are important on construction sites to ensure nonelectrical workers are isolated from the electrical worksite.

buildups will occur, particularly during switching and ground fault conditions. When there is a possibility that such dangerous induced voltage may exist, the line is worked as though it is energized. Unless the line is worked as energized, the workers on construction sites should comply with the following.

All pulling and tensioning equipment is deenergized, or more specifically, electrically isolated, insulated, or effectively grounded. On each conductor, subconductor, or conductive pulling line, 3-phase grounds are placed at increments of no more than four miles so that no worker is more than 3.2 kilometers (two miles) from a ground. Conductors, subconductors, and overhead ground wires are grounded at all deadend or catch-off points. Except for moving-type grounds, the grounds are placed and removed with a hot stick. The grounds are left in place until the entire stringing operation is completed. Such grounds are removed as the last part of the aerial cleanup. Aerial devices are grounded and bonded to conductors, subconductors, overhead ground wires, and conductive pulling lines.

Standard worker protection methods, such as barricades, ground mats, and vehicle and equipment grounding, apply to construction sites.

Using Barricades

Barricades prevent other workers from coming into contact with vehicles if they become energized accidentally. **See Figure 13-9.**

To protect workers and the public from stringing grounded systems, all vehicles and equipment at the pulling and tensioning sites, catch-off points, conductor tails, and splice areas are enclosed by a barricade. Access to vehicles and equipment, conductors, subconductors, overhead ground wires, and conductive pulling lines is accomplished by insulated platforms. If left unattended, the temporary barricades are replaced with more protective barriers and access points are closed.

Using Ground Mats

Installing portable conductive ground mats provides an equipotential zone for workers that must be on the ground around the vehicles on a construction site. The mats are preferred over insulated items because the voltage of concern often exceeds the rating of rubber gloves and other personal protective equipment, which are also cumbersome to use and easily damaged. **See Figure 13-10.**

Keeping equipment control operators on the conductive bodies of the vehicles is a protection for those workers.

Connecting Vehicles to Maintain Common Voltage

During construction, several vehicles are normally present. If they are not bonded together, different voltages may exist on each from the voltage source.

Thus, all vehicles and trailers should be connected together to maintain a common voltage. If all vehicles are bonded together and each is connected to a driven ground rod, the overall behavior is similar to a grounded overhead line with multiple neutral connections to pole down wires.

All areas become a source for step and touch potential voltages.

As in other maintenance tasks, paralleling of grounds reduces the current through a single ground. If using driven ground rods, they must be spaced twice the distance they are driven into earth. Otherwise, the shell of earth surrounding each rod overlaps the adjacent rod, reducing the effectiveness of the combination. The earth resistance is reduced as the rod is driven deeper.

MAINTENANCE PROGRAM PERFORMANCE FOR CONSTRUCTION

A maintenance program is an aid to safety during construction. Elements of the program are provided by the manufacturer, employer, and even workers.

Occupational Safety and Health Administration Standard Requirements

OSHA regulations do not specifically state that a maintenance program is required. However, such a program is implied by OSHA's "capable equipment" requirement. Protective grounding equipment shall be capable of conducting maximum fault current that could flow at the point of grounding for the time necessary to clear the fault. This equipment shall have an ampacity greater than or equal to that of No. 2 AWG copper.

Manufacturer Provisions

The manufacturer must ensure that all of its equipment meets standards and requirements. The manufacturer should provide information on the use of its equipment. It should also encourage maintenance. Finally, the manufacturer should assist customers as needed.

Utility or Employer Requirements

The utility or employer must provide training for all workers. It should also define and enforce work methods. Ideally, this is done through the development of a maintenance program. The employer or utility should also identify hazards that may be present on the construction site.

Worker Requirements

The worker's part in the maintenance program is primarily to understand the work that needs to be done and to follow the rules set down to get that work done safely. Workers should use equipment correctly and take care of it. This is done through periodic inspection and by reporting any damage.

In some cases, a grounding and jumper practice review may be justified. Situations such as increased fault current levels and increased conductors per structure or right-of-way may prompt a review. The age of the protective grounding equipment may also be a concern. Finally, if accidents happen on the construction site, and continue to occur, grounding and jumper practice is fully justified.

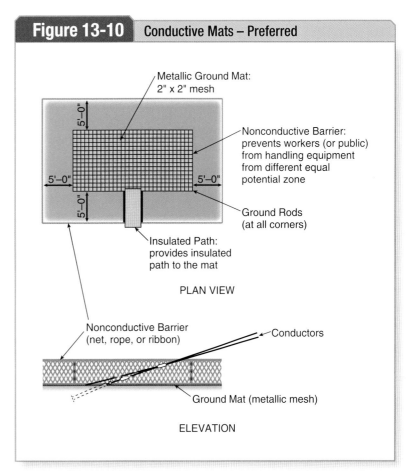

Figure 13-10. Conductive mats are ideal because they create an equipotential work zone.

Summary

Construction sites are busy places, with numerous workers and vehicles near energized lines throughout many stages of a project. Thus, they have specific requirements for vehicles and placement of workers to ensure fill protection. Sufficient barricades must be used to keep nonelectrical workers away from hazardous areas and vehicles on the construction site. Protective ground mats are also used at all needed sites. The multiple vehicles typically present at a construction site means multiple ground connections must be made. These vehicles should be connected together to avoid different voltages on each vehicle. Installation of underbuilds requires extra caution.

To ensure worker safety, maintenance programs must be followed. Before installation, equipment should be checked and maintenance should be performed as needed. Grounded lines must be maintained at all times throughout a construction project.

Review Questions

1. **A standard stringing block can be used in place of grounding traveler if the neoprene linings are removed.**
    a. True
    b. False

2. **The weak points in running grounds and traveling grounds is the interface between the __?__ .**
    a. cable wheel and grounding cable attachment point
    b. conductor and wheel contact surface
    c. grounding jumper clamp and ferrule
    d. grounding jumper and wheel axel

3. **Crews clipping conductors and overhead ground wires are protected by __?__ .**
    a. bracket grounds at the pulling and tensioning ends
    b. individual grounds connected to the phase being worked
    c. traveler grounds at the pulling end
    d. running grounds at the tension end

4. **When working on or near insulated overhead ground wires, the specified working clearance for a __?__ circuit must be maintained.**
    a. 600 V
    b. 2.4 kV
    c. 5 kV
    d. 15 kV

5. **On each conductor, subconductor, or conductive pulling line, 3-phase grounds are placed at increments so that no worker is more than __?__ from a ground.**
    a. 5,000 feet
    b. 2,000 meters
    c. 2 miles
    d. 4 kilometers

References

BIBLIOGRAPHY

1. Institute of Electrical and Electronics Engineers. ANSI/IEEE-C2, *National Electrical Safety Code.* New York: IEEE, August 1989.

2. Institute of Electrical and Electronics Engineers. Standard 516, "IEEE Guide for Maintenance Methods on Energized Power Lines." New York: IEEE, 2003.

3. Occupational Safety and Health Administration. *Code of Federal Regulations.* Title 29, part 1910, Occupational Safety and Health Standards. Subpart V, section 269, Electric Power Generation, Transmission, and Distribution. Washington, DC: U.S. Department of Labor, 1994.

4. Dalziel, C.F. "The Effects of Electric Shock on Man." *IRE Transactions on Medical Electronics* (PGME-5), May 1956. Reprinted by the U.S. Atomic Energy Commission.

5. Dalziel, C.F. "Electric Shock Hazard." *IEEE Spectrum,* February 1972, pp. 41–50.

6. Occupational Safety and Health Administration. *Code of Federal Regulations.* Title 29, part 1910, Occupational Safety and Health Standards. Subpart B, section 17, Regulations Relating to Labor. Washington, DC: U.S. Department of Labor, 1994.

7. Occupational Safety and Health Administration. *Code of Federal Regulations.* Title 29, part 1926, Safety and Health Regulations for Construction. Subpart B, section 17, Regulations Relating to Labor. Washington, DC: U.S. Department of Labor, 1987.

8. Occupational Safety and Health Administration. *Code of Federal Regulations.* Title 29, part 1926, Safety and Health Regulations for Construction. Subpart R, section 269. Washington, DC: U.S. Department of Labor, 1987.

9. American Society for Testing and Materials. Standard F855, "Standard Specifications for Temporary Protective Grounds to Be Used on De-energized Electric Power Lines and Equipment." West Conshohocken, PA: ASTM, 2000.

10. Institute of Electrical and Electronics Engineers. Paper SM-607-2 PWRD, "Factors in Sizing Protective Grounds." New York: IEEE, 1994.

11. Institute of Electrical and Electronics Engineers. Standard 1048, "Guide for Protective Grounding of Power Lines." New York: IEEE, 1990.

12. American Society for Testing and Materials. Standard F1117, "Standard Specification for Dielectric Overshoe Footwear." West Conshohocken, PA: ASTM, 1993.

13. American Society for Testing and Materials. ASTM Standard F1116, "Standard Test Method for Determining Dielectric Strength of Overshoe Footwear." West Conshohocken, PA: ASTM, 1988.

14. Erga, B. "Test Results of Grounding Uninsulated Aerial Lift Vehicles Near Energized Distribution Lines." Power Engineering Transactions SM-312-9 PWRD. New York: Institute of Electrical and Electronics Engineers, 1991.

15. Western Area Power Administration. *Protective Grounding Engineering Guidelines.* Lakewood, CO: WAPA, 2005.

16. Western Area Power Administration. *Power System Safety Manual.* Lakewood, CO: WAPA, 2001.

17. Institute of Electrical and Electronics Engineers. Standard 1246, "IEEE Guide for Temporary Protective Grounding Systems Used in Substations." New York: IEEE, 2003.

18. Institute of Electrical and Electronics Engineers. Standard 524a, "IEEE Guide to Grounding During the Installation of Overhead Transmission Line Conductors." New York: IEEE, 1992.

19. Western Area Power Administration. *Power System Operations Manual.* Lakewood, CO: WAPA, 1995.

RELATED READING

Bishop, J.H. "Protective Grounding Methods," internal paper. St. Louis, MO: Union Electric Co., February 20, 1990.

Dawalibi, F.P. "Validity of Conventional Approaches for Calculating Body Currents Resulting from Electric Shock." Institute of Electrical and Electronics Engineers, Power and Energy Society, Substations Committee. Paper presented at the IEEE/PES Winter Meeting, New York, January 31–February 5, 1988.

Erga, B., and Bonner, J.T. "Test Results of Personal Protective Grounding on Distribution Line Wood Pole Construction." IEEE Power Engineering Transactions SM-558-9. New York: Institute of Electrical and Electronics Engineers, 1988.

Fink, D.G., and Beaty, H.W., editors. *Standard Handbook for Electrical Engineers,* 13th edition. New York: McGraw-Hill, 1983.

Fink, D.G., and Carroll, J.M., editors. *Standard Handbook for Electrical Engineers,* 10th edition. New York: McGraw-Hill, 1969.

Institute of Electrical and Electronics Engineers. Paper SM-606-4 PWRD, "Methods for Protecting Employees and Others from Electrical Hazards Adjacent to Electric Utility Vehicles." New York: IEEE, 1994.

Institute of Electrical and Electronics Engineers. Standard 80, "Guide for Safety in AC Substation Grounding." New York: IEEE, 2000.

International Electrotechnical Commission. Publication 479-1, *Effects of Current Passing Through the Human Body.* Geneva, Switzerland: IEC, 1985.

James G. Biddle Instruments. *Getting Down to Earth: A Manual on Earth-Resistance Testing for the Practical Man,* Manual 25Ta, Blue Bell, PA: James G. Biddle Instruments, April 1981.

Union Electric Co. *Standard Safe Working Practices and Procedures for Union Electric Employees.* Section 5.7, "Grounding—De-energized Circuits Normally Operating from 600 Volts to 69 kV Inclusive." St. Louis, MO: Union Electric Co., 1969.

Western Area Power Administration. *A Study of Voltage Induction on Parallel Transmission Lines,* A3940 Technical Support. Lakewood, CO: WAPA, May 1984.

Western Area Power Administration. *Electromagnetic Induced Voltage Measurements During Mead Staged Fault Tests.* Lakewood, CO: WAPA, June 27, 1996.

Western Area Power Administration. *Evaluation of Four Basic Transmission Line Grounding Methods During Staged Phase to Ground Bolted Faults at Mid Distance of Kayenta Shiprock 230 kV Line.* Lakewood, CO: WAPA, August 9, 1995.

Western Area Power Administration. *Evaluation of Two Basic Transmission Line Grounding Methods During Staged Phase to Ground Bolted Faults at Structure 1/5 of the Mead Perkins 525 kV Line.* Lakewood, CO: WAPA, April 24, 1996.

Index